JANE'S
MILITARY REVIEW

edited by Ian V. Hogg

JANE'S MILITARY REVIEW

edited by Ian V. Hogg

Fifth year of issue

JANE'S

First published in 1986 by
Jane's Publishing Company Limited
238 City Road, London EC1V 2PU

Distributed in the Philippines and
the USA and its dependencies by
Jane's Publishing Inc,
115 5th Avenue
New York, NY 10003

ISBN 0 7106 0369 X

Typesetting by Method Limited
Epping, Essex

Printed in the United Kingdom by
Biddles Ltd, Guildford

Publisher's note
The first compilation in this series, published in October
1981, was issued under the title *Jane's Military Annual
1981-82*.

Contents

Foreword

For our fifth annual *Jane's Military Review* we have, as usual, cast a wide net to bring in a variety of military experts, all of whom have something interesting to offer. We should, of course, point out that these various experts are delivering their own opinions, and where they hold official posts of one sort or another, these opinions do not necessarily reflect the official opinions of their employers. The *Military Review* is a forum for opinions, and, as we have stressed before, no restraints are placed on contributors to follow any particular party line.

For that matter we follow no jingoist line either; this year we have a most interesting contribution which gives the Argentine point of view on the military actions in the Falkland Islands (or Malvinas) in 1982, based upon official Argentine documents. This should prove interesting to military students, since it is not often that one can isolate a small campaign and review the actions of both sides within such a short time of its taking place. We also have an unusual view of current pistol design as

seen from the other side of the Iron Curtain and an insight into what makes soldiers fight, a subject which admits of a number of opinions. Other contemporary subjects are the newly-formed Light Infantry Divisions of the United States Army, the ill-fated Sergeant York air defence weapon system, and the facts behind the Strategic Defense Initiative, or 'Star Wars' as it has come to be known.

We also include our usual picture reviews of new equipment and recent military exercises and the annual look-back to the days when (or so it seems today) soldiering was a rather less stressful affair.

In addition to thanking our contributors for making the *Review* as interesting as it is, we would also like to thank Alex Vanags-Baginskis and the design staff of Jane's for their hard work in turning a collection of manuscripts and photographs into a finished book, in spite of the idleness of the editor, and Derek Ballington of Jane's archives for finding many illustrations at short notice.

The Military Year

Ian V. Hogg

Sergeant York, seen at the time of its original acceptance into service.

The Federal German Army's Gepard air defence tank, seen on exercises in 1980. The surveillance radar at the rear of the turret is folded down into the travelling position.

Among the more significant military announcements of the year has been the recent decision by the US Department of Defense that the Sergeant York twin 40 mm Divisional Air Defence (DIVAD) gun system is to be abandoned after some four years of work and several millions of dollars have been poured into it. Our Washington correspondent Hugh Lucas deals with this in some detail in another part of this Review, but a few general observations are perhaps not out of place here.

One is irresistibly reminded of Mauler, an air defence system put forward in the late 1950s. At that time the wartime 40 mm L/60 Bofors guns in the hands of Britain and the USA were reaching the end of their useful life, in spite of various 'quick-fixes' which had been invented, and the search was on for a modern low-level air defence system. At that time the missile was the coming thing, guns were as obsolete as cross-bows in the minds of many defence technicians and

10

soldiers, and it seemed possible to put together a package of high-technology which would solve all the problems. Mauler promised all this and lots more; mounted on the XM546 tracked chassis (the same chassis which today carries Tracked Rapier), Mauler had a pack of 12 high-acceleration missiles, gyro-stabilised acquisition and tracking radars, power supplies and an advanced computer all within an all-up weight of just under 12 tonnes. There was a crew of two which, according to some of the advanced billing, would have little to do but drive the thing and make tea; the

radars would find targets, track them, pass them to the computer which would then assess them and fire the homing missiles at the correct moment.

As one critic later said, 'This was perhaps the greatest example of biting off more than the technology could chew'. To cut a long story short, Mauler never produced the answers it promised, even with the application of copious draughts of dollars, some of which were contributed by the British Army who hoped to adopt the system. In the event the British turned to the L/70 Bofors and were eventually rescued by the privately-

Final inspection of the SA80 rifle at the Royal Small Arms Factory, Enfield.

developed Rapier, while the Americans adopted Chaparral, an adaption of the air-to-air Sidewinder missile in the ground-to-air role.

The parallels with Sgt York are obvious, even though the latter did at least manage to get into some sort of production. Once again there was the attempt to stitch together some existing equipment with pieces of new technology in the hope that since everthing worked separately, the sum would be better than the parts. When the DIVAD gun contract was first announced, one senior defence analyst pointed to the existing Gepard twin 35 mm AA tank, adopted by Germany, Belgium and the Netherlands, and asked 'What are the

Americans trying to do? Re-invent the wheel?' One announced reason for not adopting an existing design was that Gepard could only predict a straight target course, while DIVAD would have a digital computer capable of predicting a curved course. Since then Oerlikon have improved the computer on Gepard to the point where it could probably predict accurately for an aircraft flying a zig-zag course backwards.

We doubt if even now the full story of Sgt York is in the open, or ever will be. And we should say straight away that there is no Chauvinism in our theme – the equally sordid saga of the Tigerfish torpedo should destroy any ideas of that. The lesson, learned yet again, at great expense, is that you cannot solve defence problems by simply throwing money at them, nor by giving technological whizz-kids their head. It pays to have a few practical soldiers (or sailors, or airmen) around the place to keep people's feet on the ground.

In the wake of Sergeant York's collapse there is no shortage of contenders for his replacement, though none of them offer a solely-gun solution; as one American manufacturer said recently, 'Anyone who goes near Congress in the next five years with anything that looks even remotely like Sergeant York won't stand a chance.' The preferred solution seems to be a mix of high-velocity small-calibre cannon for the close-in targets and modified Stinger missiles for the longer ranges. This has also appeared in Europe during the year; at the Paris Air Show there was a project which had been put together for Egypt which consisted of twin ex-Soviet 23 mm cannon, a pod of SA-7 Grail missiles, and a French radar and electro-optical sight, all mounted in a turret which could be fitted to any convenient armoured vehicle. The Association of the US Army Convention in Washington showed more of this sort of combination, among them the GE Defender and Blazer and the Boeing Avenger. The general consensus was to use a multiple-barrel Gatling-type cannon together with four Stinger missiles, though some of the designs showed variations which would accommodate other guns and/or missiles.

The Gulf War between Iran and Iraq continues to drag its irresolute course, with little information escaping from either country since each appears to have a paranoid distrust of foreign journalists and neither has the slightest intention of telling the truth about its exploits. Perhaps this is for the best; if the two contestants continue circling round each other like heavyweight boxers, a stalemate will be the result and that will at least not discommode anyone. An outright victory by either side would be political bad news for the West unless some mitigating circumstance were to arise, and that does not seem likely at the present time.

The inability of qualified observers to get into the fighting zone is unfortunate, since this war is one in which neither side has the slightest compunction about

The official hand-over of the first SA80 rifles at Enfield, 2 October 1985. The Arsenal employees march off carrying the old rifles, while the men of the Worcester and Sherwood Foresters Regiment hold their new weapons.

what weapons it uses or how it uses them. Scud and Frog missiles appear to have been fired quite freely into populous areas, and it would be instructive if we could discover something positive about the operation, accuracy, consistency and effect of these weapons. Rumours of poison gas abound, and there appears to be hard evidence that phosgene has been used; again, a technical point which intrigues military analysts – why phosgene? What sort of casualty ratio did it produce? What defensive measures were adopted, if any? There are also rumours and reports of a wide variety of modern weapons in use; we recall the furore in Sweden some years ago when a newspaper 'revealed' that Bofors RBS-70 air defence missiles were in use by Iraq. Not so, said Bofors, and the case remains 'not proven'. But if modern weapons are in use, what lessons are there to be drawn, what technical information to be assessed? This will perhaps strike some readers as a rather selfish attitude to

another's misfortunes; true, but there is another side to the coin. If the contestants refuse to discuss the technology, how do they know they are extracting the most from it?

An interesting side-effect of the Iran-Iraq War is the recent announcement of the formation of a Joint Arab Strike Force, named 'Peninsula Shield'. This force, made up of land, sea and air elements from the six nations forming the Gulf Cooperation Council, has begun by assembling two brigades from the Saudi Arabian army and two battalions from Kuwait and is expected to reach a final strength of something between 10,000 and 13,000 with contingents from Oman, Qatar, Bahrain, Kuwait, Saudi Arabia and the United Arab Emirates.

The proclaimed purpose of this move is the collective security of the six oil-rich nations against 'potential threats', but most observers are of the opinion that a more simple answer is that the six countries are apprehensive firstly of military attack from Iran and secondly that the whole Iran-Iraq conflict may very easily spill over into the Gulf area. Another fear is that the Iranian Shi'ite fanatics could easily move to internal

13

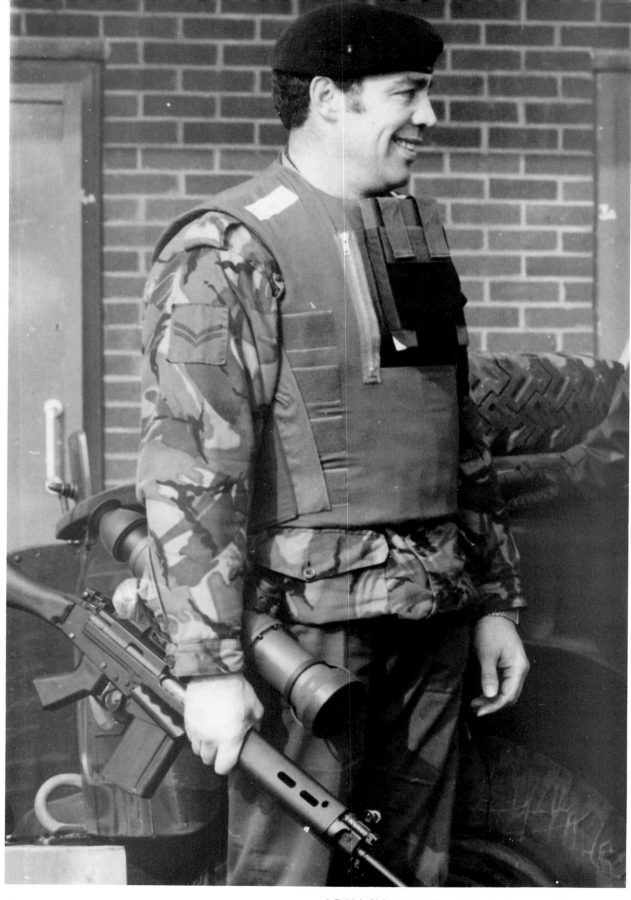

14

A British Airborne soldier wearing body armour: how long has he worn it, and how long can he continue to wear it?

dissention in the six countries and that this force could then become a counter-insurgency force of some potency.

Command of the Peninsula Shield force is currently in the hands of a Saudi general, though it has been suggested that if internal problems demand the force's use within one of the member countries, then command would devolve upon the country concerned.

Reticence is equally the role of the Soviets in Afghanistan, but the same cannot be said for their opponents the Afghan guerillas. They lose no opportunity to discuss weaponry and technicalities with anyone who has anything to offer them in the way of knowledge or analytical powers. Their latest achievement is the capture of a Soviet attack helicopter, and doubtless the defence analysts of the West are beating their way up the high hills with questionnaires, cameras and certified cheques. The Afghans, no fools, part with information and specimens of Soviet weapons only in exchange for money or money's worth, to enable them to replenish their armoury.

Study of Soviet tactics in Afghanistan shows that, after attempting to fight a Central European war they have modified their methods to what is little more than the tactics of the British Army on the North-West frontier in the late 19th/early 20th century. They advance up the valleys, picqueting the heights as they go, make their punitive gesture, and then withdraw, picqueting the heights again to cover their retreat. The only difference is that instead of marching they use armoured personnel carriers and helicopters and have a great deal more firepower.

One of the most difficult tasks for militiary historians is to indentify precisely when a particular weapon entered military service. The usual solution is to accept the 'Approval Date', but in truth this may be well divorced from the actual date on which a serving soldier first got his hands on the weapon. During a war, for example, weapons are issued without much attention being paid to the paperwork, and the Approval Date is often a year or more after there is positive identification of the weapon being in use. In peacetime the reverse is often the case and the weapon is approved long before production facilities exist; the abortive 7 mm Rifle Number 9 is a case in point – it was formally approved in 1952 but no rifles ever went into service and the approval was later cancelled.

It therefore gives us pleasure to be able to record, for the benefit of future historians, that the first Enfield 5.56 mm SA80 rifle was formally handed over by Lord Trefgarne, Minister for Munitions and Supply, on 2 October 1985, to Sgt Gavin of the 1st Battalion the Worcester & Sherwood Foresters Regiment. A small ceremony was carried out at the Royal Small Arms Factory, Enfield Lock, in which Sgt Gavin and his section arrived in an MCV-80 fighting vehicle and dismounted bearing the standard FN-FAL self-loading rifle and the FN-MAG general purpose machine gun. They formed up in line before the Minister, Sgt Gavin grounded arms and marched forward to receive his rifle, after which a file of Royal Small Arms Factory employees marched out in front of the section and handed them the new Enfield rifle and Light Support Weapon, receiving the 7.62 mm weapons in exchange. Then a file from the Royal Ordnance Factory Radway Green, the small arms ammunition factory, marched on and presented each man with a full magazine for his new weapon. Sgt Gavin and his section remounted their vehicle and drove off, and the assembled audience then fell in behind the band of the Worcester & Sherwood Foresters and marched (in a manner of speaking) to the sound of martial music to the firing range to see the new weapons demonstrated. An unusual ceremony, but then new rifles don't appear in the British Army every day of the week and it was worth marking the occasion.

Although the American M16A2 rifle is just beginning to issue to the US Army, it is already the subject of an 'enhancement programme', which, it has just been revealed, began as far back as April 1984. This programme does not address itself to any mechanical features of the rifle but is concerned with adding an optical sight.

Optical sights on infantry rifles have suddenly become interesting; when the British Army proposed such a sight, built into the carrying handle, on the EM2 rifle of the late 1940s, the response was mixed. Theorists allowed that it might be a good idea, but most other people recoiled in horror at the thought of putting such an expensive and delicate device into the hands of the soldier. In the middle 1970s the Austrian Army adopted the Steyr AUG rifle, with a 1.4x telescope built into the carrying handle, and saw its rifle marksmanship take a sharp upward curve. At about the same time the British adopted the SUIT (Sight Unit, Infantry, Trilux) sight in small numbers. This was a 4-power telescope with a good field of view and with the aiming mark illuminated by a long-life Tritium source. Not only did it improve daylight shooting, but the illuminated mark and better light-gathering allowed an extension of the infantryman's working day by giving him better visibility in dawn and dusk conditions. More recently the British Army has adopted SUSAT (Sight Unit, Small Arm, Trilux) a somewhat improved version of SUIT, as the standard infantry sight for the new Enfield rifle.

All this activity has attracted attention elsewhere, and the US Army has decided to investigate the possibility of improving the hit probability of the infantryman by giving him an optical sight. The Canadian Army is also looking at the same problem and is currently testing a sight made by Leitz of Canada, so the US testing authority has acquired a Leitz sight, a British SUSAT, a Swedish Aimpoint reflex collimating sight, and two

Leupold sighting telescopes in order to conduct a comparative trial. Ten US Marines and 28 US Army soldiers have now fired some 110,000 rounds in an extended test, but the results have yet to be assessed.

However, preliminary indications have shown some interesting points; in unstressed situations – ie a target range where the shooter can take as long as he likes about aiming and firing – there seems to be little advantage in using an optical sight over conventional iron sights. This may surprise some target shooters and hunters, but recall that here the object is combat shooting, not precision marksmanship; a hit on a man-sized target is a hit, whether it goes into the ten-ring or elsewhere. Under simulated stress – shooting after violent exercise, against the clock – there seems little advantage at short ranges but a significant improvement in hits when using optical sights at long range.

The final question is whether or not the improvement in performance is going to justify the cost of an optical sight – which, in some cases, can be almost as much as the rifle upon which it is mounted. And so far the Americans have not been able to find any positive factor in one direction or the other.

As these lines are being written, there comes the news of the American adoption of Rita, the French battlefield communications system, in preference to Ptarmigan, the British equivalent. The popular press has treated the story as a major disaster for British manufacturers and has made much of Mrs Thatcher's presumed intervention, but the truth seems to be rather more mundane. If, as is reported, the British price was some 70 percent higher than the French, small wonder that the Americans made the choice they did. The General Administration Office of Congress would have descended like the proverbial ton of bricks on anyone paying two or three billion dollars over the odds, especially after the Sergeant York fiasco and the manifold stories of $600 hammers and gold-plated can-openers which have regaled us over the past few years.

The important question which needs to be answered is why the British tender was so very much higher than the French for what, by all the reports, was a broadly comparable system. One factor will doubtless be that since the French system has been in use for some time, most of the development costs will have been amortised by this time, whereas the British contract must have had to take this into account. But even this cannot entirely cover the enormous gap. A recent television programme suggested that the French company must have been subsidised by their government so as to be able to quote a low price; this is not impossible, though frankly we doubt it. What is certain is that the French government gets behind its armaments industry and helps it to sell, and it also gives useful tax and similar financial concessions to those who make and export defence equipment. This sort of encouragement goes far to help the manufacturers to quote highly competitive prices, but it still cannot account for the massive discrepancy in this case.

A new spectre has arisen to haunt quartermasters and equipment officers. The Du Pont company, makers of the Aramid fibre which forms the basis of all flexible body armour, has announced that their researches show that this armour has a useful life of, at the most, five years, after which it will require to be replaced. It appears that there is no deterioration of the fabric as such, but the constant flexing and wrinkling to which the garment is subjected in its life gradually weakens the fibres to the point where they will no longer stop bullets or fragments. The only solutions appear to be to take more care of the garments when not being worn, and make them with some form of semi-rigid support which will prevent wrinkling. One supposes that bullet-proof vests, in the future, will bear labels similar to those on packets of cheese in the supermarket – 'Best before 12/90'. One is also inclined to wonder just how long some of the flak jackets and other armoured garments in military use around the world have been in service.

SDI – Origins, Objectives and Achievements

Dexter Jerome Smith

Like a bolt from the blue, one Wednesday night in March 1983 President Reagan made a broadcast from the White House that was to have a profound effect – an effect on superpower politics, on military strategy and on inter-Alliance relations – ultimately an effect even on global security. Mr Reagan chose that moment to share, in his own words, 'a vision of the future which offers hope . . . that we embark on a programme to counter the awesome Soviet missile threat with measures that are defensive'.

The aim of this effort, he said, was twofold: to strengthen deterrence and make nuclear weapons 'impotent and obsolete'. Not surprisingly it was the second of these two aims that attracted most attention, and very rapidly the debate sparked by the President's remarks began to centre on whether there could ever really be a perfect defence against ballistic nuclear missiles.

This idea ran so counter to the conventional wisdom that sceptics were not hard to find. Senator Edward Kennedy encapsulated the mood of exasperation and disbelief expressed by many when he pinned to the President's scheme early on the 'Star Wars' label that has stuck to it ever since.

Nevertheless, the Strategic Defence Initiative, as it was later officially named, has persisted, and converts have been won over. The apparent inconsistencies between the President's two objectives – strengthening deterrence and doing away with the nuclear deterrent – have not helped Mr Reagan's case, but slowly the messsage has begun to get across that his objectives may be reconciled by seeing the former as SDI's short-to-medium term goal and the latter as the programme's long term aim.

Mr Reagan recently married his two objectives together during an interview with the French newspaper *Le Figaro* in these terms: 'Effective defences against ballistic missiles have the potential for enhancing deterrence by increasing an aggressor's uncertainties and helping reduce *or eliminate* the apparent military value of nuclear attack to an aggressor. In our SDI research we seek to reduce the incentives – now or in the future – for Soviet aggression and thereby to ensure effective deterrence for the long term'.

The confusion that still exists over SDI's real aim is at least in part due to the fact that SDI at present is nothing more than a research and development programme, and science has yet to reveal fully what it is capable of achieving in this field. As it is, however, some critics, focusing on increased emphasis put on the programme's role in strengthening deterrence, see in this evidence of some deep split between the President and the rest of his Administration – Mr Reagan being just about the only one in Washington really believing nuclear weapons can be done away with.

Received Wisdom

Regardless of which SDI objective is being pushed hardest by the Reagan Administration, winning converts to SDI has proven a particularly difficult task if for no other reason than that there remains a perfectly respectable view – a view that the President, his Cabinet colleagues and aides all previously supported – a view on which there was broad overarching consensus – that for 40 years the existence of nuclear weapons and their terrible destructive power has helped keep the peace for the United States and its NATO allies.

According to the conventional wisdom, America – the only country ever to use 'the bomb' in war, and then to stop a war rather than initiate one – is able to offer a security guarantee to those willing to shelter under its nuclear umbrella.

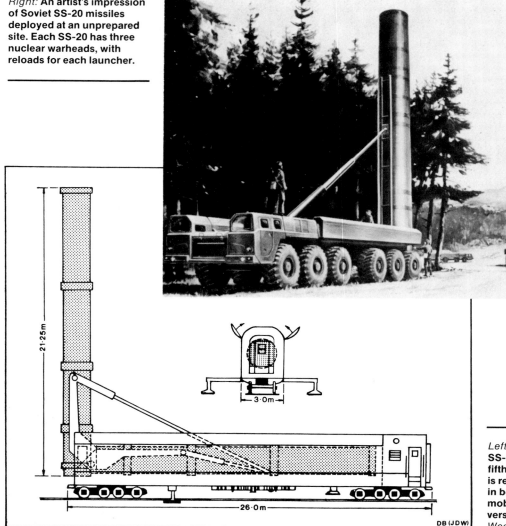

Right: **An artist's impression of Soviet SS-20 missiles deployed at an unprepared site. Each SS-20 has three nuclear warheads, with reloads for each launcher.**

21·25 m

3·0 m

26·0 m

DB (JDW)

Left: **Diagram of rail-mobile SS-X-4 operation. This new fifth generation Soviet ICBM is reportedly being evolved in both silo-based and mobile (transportable) versions.** (*Jane's Defence Weekly*)

True, two US allies – Britain and France – felt it necessary to develop their own nuclear weapons, but that only adds to the security of the Western Alliance today – an aggressor now has three instead of one decision-making centre to take account of.

True, the Soviets soon developed their own nuclear weapons, and showed they were capable of racing the Americans, catching up and even in some cases surpassing them, but that just reinforces the ultimate deterrent value of nuclear weapons as a rough balance of terror has been struck.

True, China's acquisition of 'the bomb' raised the spectre of nuclear weapons profileration, but China's bomb seems more a problem for the Soviets than the West, and the nuclear Non-Proliferation Treaty signed by all five nuclear weapons states in 1968 seems to have held.

Nuclear deterrence by this argument has come of age; some even speak of there being such a thing as 'extended deterrence' – the nuclear threat deterring conventional conflicts even in far away places – though here they seem to conveniently forget Vietnam, Angola, the Horn of Africa, and, most recently, Afghanistan.

The centrepiece of the conventional wisdom is the doctrine of Mutual Assured Destruction (MAD), which begins with the premise that it is not in the interests of either the Warsaw Pact or NATO to pick a fight because were there to be a full nuclear exchange the outcome would be the annihilation of both sides. In essence, the MAD doctrine says to an aggressor: If you attack me, you may kill me but I'll take you with me to the grave.

NATO's strategy of 'flexible response' in part underlines the MAD doctrine by setting out a framework within which NATO could and would

An example of a directed-energy weapon is this space-based laser system, capable of intercepting ballistic missiles before they can deploy their warheads and decoys. (*US Department of Defense*)

escalate a conflict once started through the point of first use of nuclear weapons up to and including a full exchange of nuclear arsenals.

The 1979/1983 decision to deploy American medium-range nuclear missiles in Europe (cruise and Pershings) was dictated by NATO's desire to have an adequate response to Soviet medium-range nuclear missiles (SS-20s) so that the Soviets, if they were to prevail in war, would be forced to go to the next and ultimate stage of firing their Intercontinental Ballistic Missiles (ICBMs) at the US. NATO wanted an equivalent to the SS-20 because it feared if the Soviets used SS-20s the Alliance might be forced to give in short of an all-out nuclear war, the Americans preventing further escalation unless and until mainland America was attacked with Soviet ICBMs – the Americans fearing provoking just such an attack.

Doubts

Philosophically, Ronald Reagan has never taken to the MAD doctrine even though in the absence of something better he has felt obliged to support it. In 1976, when he was making his first run for Presidency, Mr Reagan told his military advisor, newly retired US Army General Daniel Graham, that he felt there had to be an alternative to the nuclear suicide pact which made the Soviets co-guarantors of America's security. Mr Reagan

DoD Weighs In

What really tipped the balance with the Pentagon was their realisation that despite the decision to underwrite the doctrine of Mutual Assured Destruction with the decision to deploy ground-launched cruise missiles (GLCMs) and Pershing 2s in Europe the assumptions behind MAD were visably breaking down. For the MAD doctrine to hold it was necessary for each side to have a sufficiently large retaliatory force to destroy the other, and it was necessary for both to believe that the next world war would be nuclear and unlimited, with each convinced that the other was prepared to fight to the point of destruction.

The writings of the then Chief of the Soviet General Staff, Marshal Ogarkov, are of particular interest here because they suggest the Soviet Union may not believe in the MAD doctrine at all – after all MAD was not a Soviet concept; rather it was the invention of Robert McNamara while he was US Secretary for Defense in the mid-1960s. Marshal Ogarkov claims that Soviet society would be capable of withstanding a nuclear conflict of far greater intensity than the United States or Europe could endure. Moreover, he suggests that were Soviet forces ever to fight NATO forces they should attempt to rapidly advance deep into NATO territory and hug NATO forces so as to make it more difficult for NATO to use nuclear weapons for fear of hitting their own troops or their own civilian populations.

As to MAD's requirement that both sides maintain a nuclear retaliatory force sufficiently large to ensure the destruction of the other side (even after the other side had launched a first strike nuclear attack), this has had the effect of leading both the USA and USSR into a horrendously costly arms race.

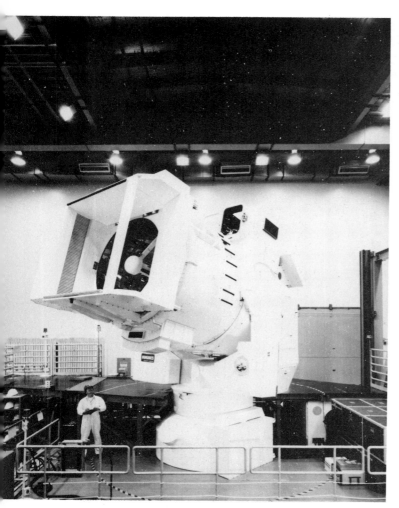

A US Navy High Energy Laser Beam director, designed to track targets in flight and direct a high-powered laser beam to selected aimpoints. It is intended to link this with a High-Energy chemical laser to gain experience in integrating laser with director. (*US Department of Defense*)

The First Strike Threat

The large missile overkill potential each side built up was seen as the only real hedge against the other side launching a pre-emptive nuclear strike. In 1972 both sides signed the Anti-Ballistic Missile (ABM) Treaty to help make possible some limitation in nuclear arms. The rationale for the Treaty was that by limiting the number and type of anti-missile defences it would be possible to limit the size of the overkill potential built into each side's nuclear arsenal.

The Pentagon believed that General Graham's advocacy of a largely space-based ballistic missile defence system was right because the effectiveness of the ABM Treaty has been eroded by the development of faster, more accurate missiles capable of carrying multiple independently targetable warheads. With both sides' first strike potential thus enhanced there was a greater risk of war. In a time of tension one side or the

set General Graham (a former Director of the Defense Intelligence Agency) the task of finding an alternative to the MAD doctrine that would allow the US to 'step off the nuclear treadmill' while still guaranteeing the security of the United States and its allies.

It took General Graham five years to flush out fully ideas on how to replace mutual assured destruction with mutual assured survival, by which time Mr Reagan had succeeded in his quest to become President. Several more months were spent working on a final report and filling in the detail before the idea was turned over to the Pentagon for their consideration of what General Graham was now calling 'High Frontier'.

It took a full year before the Joint Chiefs of Staff communicated their approval to the President. Within days Mr Reagan was to make his famous 'Star Wars' speech.

An artist's impression of a space-based mirror used to reflect a laser beam fired from the ground at attacking missiles over the horizon. (*US DoD*)

other might be 'forced' to fire first in a use-it or lose-it situation, or else one side might simply launch a first strike by design with the intention of decapitating the other side's command, control, communications and intelligence network so as to make impossible any effective retaliation.

The Pentagon pointed to the Soviet Union's 308 SS-18s with ten independently targetable warheads and her 360 SS-19s with six independently targetable warheads. Both are thought to be accurate to within 250 yards of their target. With a force of this size and accuracy the Chairman of the Joint Chiefs of Staff, US Army General John Vessey, estimated a pre-emptive Soviet strike on America's Minuteman missile silos could destroy 70 to 75 per cent, even where those silos had been 'hardened'.

Note was taken too of the Soviets developing a 'fifth generation' of ICBMs – the rail-mobile SS-24 and the road-mobile SS-25 – said to be accurate to within 125 yards. With that kind of accuracy 90 to 95 per cent of America's land-based ICBMs could be destroyed in their silos in a pre-emptive strike.

Clearly, the closer a warhead explodes to its target the greater the probability of that target being destroyed, and the Pentagon knew full well that further improvements in accuracy were both possible and likely –

America's Pershing 2 medium-range missiles now deployed in West Germany are accurate to within 30 yards!

What SDI has to offer here, therefore, is a means by which to decrease the likelihood of there being a pre-emptive first strike by reducing the probability of a particular missile hitting a particular target. In this respect it is not necessary for SDI's shield to be 100 per cent leakproof. General Graham went so far as to suggest that we could have a leaky but to all intents and purposes effective

Putting It All Together

However, the Pentagon's SDI programme is much more ambitious. It pulls together many projects begun long before SDI came on the scene and combines them with new ideas incorporating exotic and still unproven technologies yet to demonstrate practical and affordable applications. The reason why SDI seems to focus on dozens of these exotic sounding concepts – chemical lasers, gas-dynamic lasers, X-ray lasers, particle beams, hyper-velocity electromagnetic railguns, 'smart' bullets, radio-frequency weapons, etc. – is twofold. First, SDI is a research programme – we still do no know enough to say definitely this system is better than that system. Second, given that none of the systems will yield a perfect defence it is logical to want to maximise whatever defence is offered by stringing systems together – overlapping them in layers to use what is available to greatest effect in plugging holes.

Even before the President's March 1983 'Star Wars' speech the US Army and Air Force had successfully tested both ground-based lasers and airborne lasers to shoot down drones, missiles-in-tow and Sidewinder air-to-air missiles travelling around 2000 mph – about one sixth the speed of an Intercontinental Ballistic Missile.

During the Carter Administration in the late 1970s a research project was begun at the National Laboratory, Los Alamos into the development of high energy X-ray lasers. By the time Mr Reagan had come to office, the Los Alamos team led by Dr Edward Teller had already made great progress in taking a small controlled nuclear explosion, converting the energy produced into X-ray laser beams and projecting these over great distances. However, President Reagan's preference for non-nuclear space defence has caused the project to be put on the back-burner, though it has not been dropped because it is believed the Soviets are working on a similar system.

Another Carter programme brought into SDI by the Pentagon was the USAF's Homing Overlay Experiment. In June 1984 the experiment was completed with the so-called HOE Test which demonstrated that an ICBM could be shot down more than 100 miles above the Earth by an infra-red guided interceptor missile fired some 4500 miles away with the two colliding with a combined closing speed of 22,000 mph.

However, even in the case of the new SDI exotic technology projects rapid progress has been made. By early 1985 the Pentagon were able to announce that the SDI technologies test programme involving NASA's

space defence shield that would significantly reduce the risk of first strike by deploying off-the-shelf technology today.

No less an authority than Dr Robert Jastrow, the founder of NASA's Goddard Institute for Space Studies has observed: 'Nuclear bombs do not go off very readily: elaborate arrangements and a great deal of fragile electronics are needed to make one explode . . . a small charge of TNT, or a cluster of high-speed metal pellets, will usually be sufficient to disarm the bomb's mechanism'.

A 17-foot-long antisatellite missile pictured seconds after its launch from a US Air Force F-15A Eagle fighter on 13 September 1985. This test firing marked the first time a US ASAT weapon was used against a live satellite in space. The test was a complete success. The target destroyed was a redundant US satellite in orbit 320 miles up. (*US DoD*)

space shuttle would be brought forward two years because progress in the initial stages had exceeded all expectations.

Within a matter of months American astronauts had deployed the Shuttle's first military payload and demonstrated they could construct a platform in space. Furthermore, in June 1985 a laser beam was successfully fired at a target similar to a car wing-mirror mounted on the Shuttle in orbit some 220 miles up.

Back on the ground, in September 1985, the National Laboratory at Los Alamos reported their first successful test firing of a particle beam device. Research into so-called directed-energy weapons of this kind has been going on in the Soviet Union since the late 1960s and is now well advanced. Indeed, the Soviets were the first to make a major breakthrough on particle beam weapons with the invention of an ion neutraliser called a radio-frequency quadrupole.

Also in September 1985, the US Army fired a low-powered ground-based laser which held and tracked a high flying missile through its flight adjusting for atmospheric distortions as it left the Earth's atmosphere, and later again when it returned.

The basic concepts involved in the SDI programme were rigorously examined through 1983 by an independent Commission ordered by President Reagan under the Chairmanship of former NASA Director Dr Jim Fletcher, which brought together 40 of America's top scientists in this field. Many were sceptical initially but despite strenuous efforts by the Commission's 'Red Team' tasked to shoot down proposals, they unanimously concluded that no technical impediments stood in the way of achieving an effective layered ballistic missile defence shield.

The backing of the Fletcher Commission was key in getting Congressional approval for SDI's R & D effort. Congress has approved the Pentagon's plan to set aside $26 billion for the programme through to 1990.

The Programme Breakdown

Currently, sensor research accounts for about 50 percent of total SDI funds. After the boost-phase launch of an enemy missile the target goes 'cold', jettisoning its 'hot' booster so infra-red, ie. heat-seeking sensors only work optimally for boost-phase intercepts or in the terminal phase where a missile warhead heats up on re-entry into the Earth's atmosphere. Other otpical sensors of course can and would be used positioned deep in space to make them less vulnerable to attack. Many would have the facility to fire a low-powered laser beam at potential targets to help with their precise location and discriminate between decoys and real warheads. By pulsing targets with directed energy beams and measuring how much they move as a result it is possible to determine their mass, which is the real acid test since if you increase the weight of decoys they become just as expensive to launch as a real warhead.

Target Destruction programmes take some 40 per cent of SDI funds, with the focus on both directed energy weapons – space- and ground-based lasers, X-ray lasers, and particle beams, all operating at or near the speed of light, as well as kinetic energy weapons – electromagnetic railguns, 'smart' bullets, and anti-missile missiles, whose destructiveness comes from the force of impact with the enemy missile/warhead.

Directed energy weapons have the drawback that they can only fire at targets that can be seen; to space-based systems of this type missiles below cloud cover are 'invisible'. As for kinetic energy weapons the limiting factor is their velocity or lack of it: a really effective space-based hypervelocity gun would have to be able to fire projectiles at tens of kilometres per second, and this in turn would require the availability of large power supplies. However, in space heavy power-plants would become weightless and there is also the possibility of projecting energy from the ground with the use of large mirrors in space.

The remaining ten per cent of the SDI budget goes on perfecting Battle Management technologies capable of managing a battle that might involve hundreds of thousands of objects and lasts only a few minutes. Dr George Keyworth, the President's former Chief Scientific Advisor, has said he expects Mr Reagan will still be in office to see the prototype of a four megabit RAM micro-chip – the key to a fifth generation computer whose 'artificial intelligence' should satisfy SDI battle management requirements for computer-assisted programming and check-out. Here also the path-breaking work of Professor Desmond Smith of Britain's Heriot-Watt University in the field of optical (high speed) computing techniques may ultimately unlock the door.

As for software, Dr Jastrow has pointed out that 'the software for SDI will require about 10 million lines of code. However, this has already been surpassed in length and complexity by the AT and T program which controls the nation's (America's) telephone network. That has 50 million lines of code. Also, the number of interconnections between 'nodes', ie. nerve centres, in the AT and T program is 14,000, whereas the number of interconnections in the SDI program is estimated to be about 4500'.

SDI Participation by Allies

SDI has created such a multiplicity of new requirements (and this is augmented by the need for a layered system of defence) that there are going to be many opportunities for defence contractors to win contracts with the US DoD. President Reagan and Defense Secretary Weinberger have made it clear that they want some of these contracts to go to non-US companies, ie. to share the benefits of the programme with America's allies.

In December 1985 Britain became the first of America's allies to sign a Memoradum of Understanding with the US Defense Department on SDI participation (formally accepting the American SDI participation offer). West Germany soon followed suit.

Besides Professor Desmond Smith's optical computing research, the Pentagon's SDI Office has already expressed interest in work being done on an electromagnetic railgun at the Royal Armament R & D Establishment at Fort Halstead, Kent, designed for use as a possible anti-tank and anti-aircraft weapon. Another British project of interest to the Americans is British Aerospace's HOTOL – a horizontal take-off and landing space shuttle for the 1990s with a revolutionary, super-efficient new propulsion system designed by Rolls Royce that could transform the economics of space missions.

As for Germany, the gas dynamic laser being perfected by the Messerschmitt-BB company is worthy of note. It has precisely the characteristics that would be required for a terminal phase or point defence against incoming missiles.

There is still much concern, however, especially in Europe, as to whether SDI would really enhance the security of those who are closest to the Soviet Union and whose worry is thus not ICBMs but short- and medium-range nuclear missiles and tactical nuclear missiles.

In fact, longer medium-range missiles like the SS-20 and SS-22 do spend the greatest part of their flight outside of the Earth's atmosphere and so are vulnerable to space-based weapons; and as for the other medium-to-short-range nuclear weapons, some authorities think that paradoxically these might be easier to deal with than ICBMs. First, these weapons spend most of their time in the Earth's atmosphere so decoys are less of a problem because being lightweight they move slower being subject to greater air resistance. Second, they fly more slowly; and third, being smaller missiles they have smaller payloads, which means fewer warheads and fewer decoys.

Nevertheless, it is because of uncertainties in this area that some governments, like that of France, have publicly come out against SDI. However, the situation is very fluid – we are still in the proving phase, and the proof of the pudding is in the eating. In this regard it is interesting to note that the view in Washington is that in three years time we will probably see French defence companies winding up with the biggest non-US share of SDI R & D contracts.

Military Pistols

A Warsaw Pact View

Vladimir Svimbersky

The following article was submitted by a ballistics expert who recently decided that living in the West was preferable. It shows some different points of view about areas which still generate argument in many military and civil circles in the West, and although some of the ground has been covered in these pages before, we think that his views are of such interest that they are worth reading in their entirety.

In discussing the military aspects of the personal defence weapon – the pistol – one automatically excludes the revolver, since it is now generally accepted that the revolver belongs to the police service. There are exceptions to this rule, but their statistical weight is very small when considering the whole.

The reasons why the pistol was developed at all and why it probably will last for a long time in the future are extremely broad and complex. One can name tactical, technical, even pyschological reasons. The author James Jones has described reasons why many soldiers want a pistol, in his famous short story 'The Pistol', so realistically that it is very difficult to add anything of value.

The need for a small, light weapon for personal defence and very limited offensive purposes was clearly evident and with the adoption of new sophisticated crew-served equipments it is even more evident. And hand in hand with the development of the pistol itself it is possible to trace an effort to improve its rather limited (from the military point of view) capabilities. It is interesting to note that opinions about what is an 'ideal'

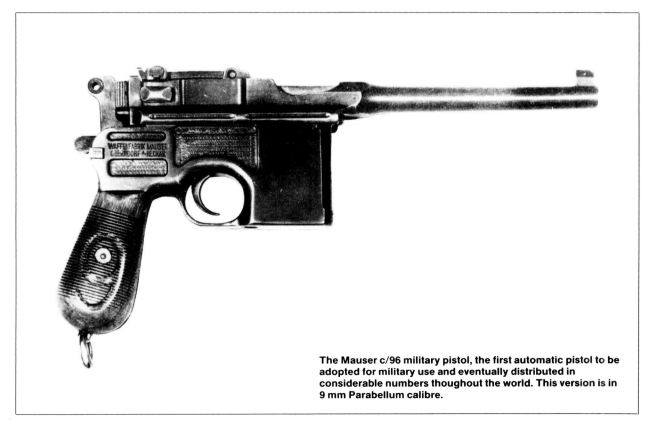

The Mauser c/96 military pistol, the first automatic pistol to be adopted for military use and eventually distributed in considerable numbers thoughout the world. This version is in 9 mm Parabellum calibre.

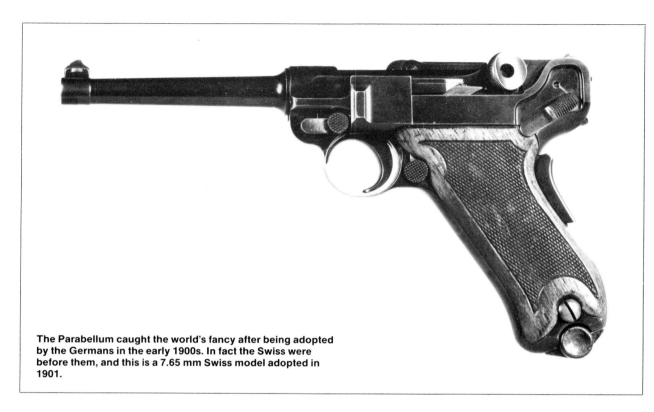

The Parabellum caught the world's fancy after being adopted by the Germans in the early 1900s. In fact the Swiss were before them, and this is a 7.65 mm Swiss model adopted in 1901.

The American Colt M1911 (*bottom*) and M1911A1 (*above*), showing the minor changes in the later model.

military handgun can be so very different. For this reason a soldier in the field can carry anything from a more or less good pistol to a weapon which reflects nothing more than some very subjective theories of military bureaucrats. In many cases, on the other hand, there are commercial handguns which have proved to be very successful as martial weapons.

The situation is similar when military handgun ammunition is discussed; and when adequate calibre and power are judged disagreements are far deeper. This latter fact shows us very clearly that tactical opinions on the military use of handguns are anything but united.

A short historical trip is necessary as an introduction to the problem. For many reasons we can start with the Mauser M1896 as the first 'true' military pistol. Though rather clumsy and expensive to manufacture, it brought at least three interesting features into general knowledge: the detachable shoulder stock/holster, the box magazine just in front of the trigger guard, and a powerful cartridge of bottle-necked shape. Of course there can be objections reflecting a strictly historical point of view against the statement above, but for practical reasons it can be accepted. Next came, roughly contemporary, what later became the German Pistole

'08 (the Luger) and the US M1911 (Colt) pistols. The German pistol on the positive side had a perfectly angled and shaped grip and loaded chamber indicator/extractor that could be felt in the dark. Its 9 mm straight walled cartridge later became standard for nearly all military pistols and sub-machine guns. Unfortunately these positive features were more than counterbalanced by its numerous disadvantages: the complexity of the design made the pistol difficult and expensive to manufacture and not very reliable under field conditions. On the other hand the countless variants that have been manufactured during the years make it the most desirable of all military pistols for the collector. This fact, of course, does not make any better military gun of it. The US M1911 of John Browning's design is the first modern military pistol, an archetypal milestone for many very good followers. Here, for the first time, a pistol appeared that had all the basic features that make an excellent handgun. The very clean design with minimum of parts, simple locking system and good feel in the hand all were put together extremely well. The chosen cartridge, the .45 ACP, nevertheless made the M1911 a little too heavy and bulky.

Between the wars four interesting military pistols were created. First and the most important was

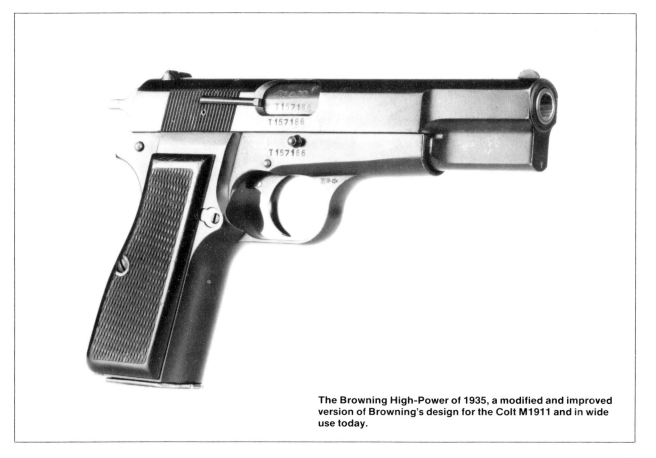

The Browning High-Power of 1935, a modified and improved version of Browning's design for the Colt M1911 and in wide use today.

29

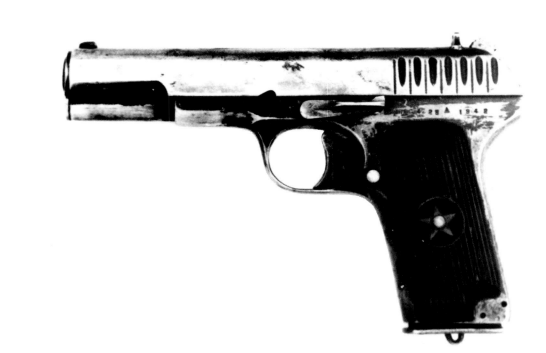

The Soviet TT-33 Tokarev, based on Browning's design but with modifications to suit Soviet production facilities.

The Polish Radom wz/35, yet another modification of Browning's basic design.

Browning's design manufactured by FN a considerably modified basic M1911 model, now in 9 mm Parabellum with 13-shot magazine and improved (simplified) locking/unlocking mechanism. The second was the Soviet pistol TT-33, an intelligently simplified variant of the M1911. Unfortunately its human engineering is very poor (notably the shape and angle of the grip) and in combination with the Soviet's powerful version of the 7.63 × 25 mm Mauser cartridge it is hardly pleasant to shoot. Nor is the quality of manufacture consistent. In spite of these facts the TT-33 is probably the best and least eclectic of all Soviet pistol designs until recently.

The third notable design was the Polish indigenous modification of the basic Browning, the wz35 pistol, popularly known as the Radom. Its locking/unlocking mechanism is even simpler than that of the FN pistol, but the magazine holds only 8 rounds. Because of the well-shaped grip the pistol sits very naturally in the shooter's hand.

In this pre-Second World War period we can trace a phenomenon that could be described as a form of cartridge schizophrenia. The US Armed Forces were happy with their big .45 ACP round, some armies used medium sized rounds such as the 9 mm Parabellum (Germany, Belgium) or 7.62 mm Tokarev (USSR). The third group of countries used the even lower-powered .380 ACP (9 mm Browning Short) for their pistols. The strangest combination was probably that used in

Czechoslovakia in the relatively complicated locked-breech vz.24 pistol that fired the .380 ACP round.

Shortly before the Second World War Germany introduced a very interesting pistol which, directly or indirectly, has influenced pistol design until quite recently. Naturally, the pistol in question is the Walther P38. Its design incorporates more or less all the features which are considered necessary in every pistol design of today: double action lockwork, automatic safety locking the firing pin, safe decocking device and loaded-chamber indicator. Rather suprisingly this complicated design proved to be relatively reliable. Ergonomic qualities are good with the exception of the double-action trigger pull which is too heavy – an inherent feature of all Walther's double-action pistols.

The Second World War brought nothing new in the field of handgun design. All the powers that were involved in the conflict had enough troubles in maintaining pistol production at the necessary level and none of the new models developed in the war years even passed the experimental stage. It is a matter of interest that quantities of revolvers were manufactured and used by the Allies during the war to alleviate the shortage of semi-automatic pistols.

After the war there were enough pistols in the inventories of all major armies and nobody wanted to spend money on such a relatively unimportant weapon. Nethertheless, some lessons had been learned and

The Czech vz/27 pistol used a complicated rotating-barrel system to lock the breech, yet fired only the 7.65 mm ACP cartridge.

The Walther P38 in its wartime form; as the P1 it still serves several armies.

The Smith & Wesson Model 39 introduced the double-action concept into American major calibre pistols.

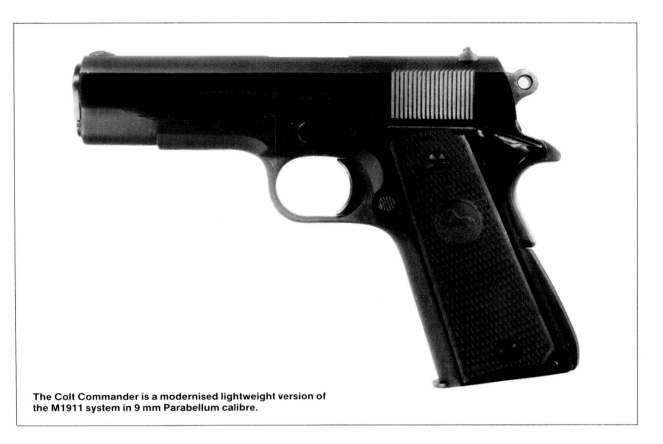

The Colt Commander is a modernised lightweight version of the M1911 system in 9 mm Parabellum calibre.

ordnance departments did not entirely sleep. It is interesting to follow how the various departments approached the problem; the general feeling was that 'something lighter and smaller is needed'.

In the USA the Infantry Board wrote military specifications for a new pistol. It was to be 9 mm in calibre, light in weight, and have the double-action feature. The research, development and testing work was later terminated without any decision being reached. The results were, at least, beneficial to the civilian handgun market; they brought about the Smith & Wesson M39 and Colt Commander families of pistols.

The USSR went even further. The Soviet experts decided that something less powerful than their 7.62 mm Tokarev or the 9 mm Parabellum would be good enough. Something that did not require a locked breech while its slide mass would be within acceptable limits for a handgun. Not very complicated calculation led them to the 9 mm Makarov round that was issued in the early 1950s. The theories of some authors, that the 9 mm Makarov is modelled on the pre-war German 9 mm Ultra round is not supported by any hard evidence. Handguns in the Soviet Army during the Second World War were not considered very important for two main reasons. Firstly, handgun marksmanship was never stressed in the USSR armed forces, and more important, Soviet officers were issued with far more

effective sub-machine guns[1]. This could lead to the conclusion, bearing in mind that the AK assault rifles began issue soon after the war, that a round slightly more powerful than .380 ACP and a pistol of blowback DA design could fulfil their needs. The new 9 mm Makarov pistol had its basic design features based on the Walther PP pistol, though not copied from it. It is a matter of interest that the Makarov pistol is of rather complex design and not very easy to manufacture, a considerable departure from the previous extremely simple Tokarev TT-33 pistol.

The USSR had switched to the 9 mm Makarov round at the same time as many armies were issuing more powerful rounds such as the 9 mm Parabellum or 7.62 mm Tokarev instead of the .380 ACP. The world map of pistol cartridges changed a little in the early 1950s: USA and USSR with .45 ACP and 9 mm Makarov

[1] Soviet officers were (and are) issued SMGs besides their pistols and there was a tendency to equip tank crew members with SMGs rather than with pistols. Probable reasons are two:
(1) Soviet SMGs were easier and cheaper to manufacture than pistols.
(2) SMG firepower is higher than that of pistol and greater effective range – about 200 m for 7.62 mm Tokarev fired from SMG.

The East German copy of the Soviet 9 mm Makarov pistol.

The Soviet Stechkin, fitted with its shoulder stock.

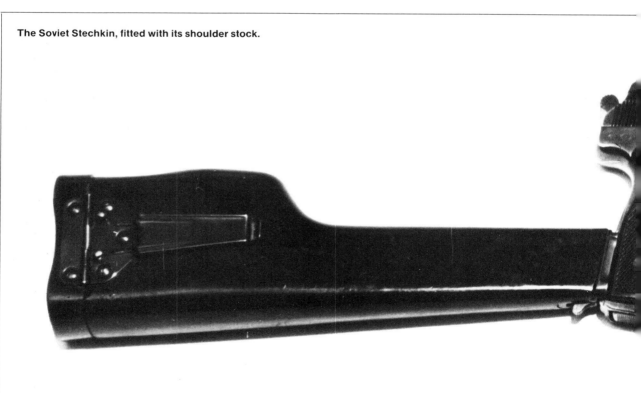

The Mauser 'Schnellfeuer' full-automatic pistol which, with the addition of a shoulder stock, could function as a sub-machine gun.

respectively as the extreme flanks of the front line, while the 'main force' consisted of 9 mm Parabellum (non-Soviet countries) and of 7.62 mm Tokarev (Soviet bloc countries and China). This is, of course, something of a generalisation; there were a few exceptions.

It could be interesting to note that on the Soviet side the 9 mm Makarov round was an 'active' choice, while on the US side the enthusiasm for the new lightweight pistols disappeared when the Army looked at the cost of such a switch and the stockpile of .45s.

The rest of the world fired 9 mm Parabellum ammunition, mainly in the FN/Browning GP35 and the Walther P38, plus a few others. On the Soviet side the situation was far simpler: the TT-33 of Tokarev and the single exception of the rather odd Czechoslovakian vz52 pistol.

Into this period of time falls the first hybrid small arm that was issued, the Stechkin APS machine pistol. Though not the first such weapon developed – the best known of its predecessors is Mauser's 'Schnellfeuer' pistol – the APS had both single and full automatic fire capability and a detachable shoulder stock/holster. Issued in the early 1950s the gun disappeared silently from the service in the early 1970s. It was of rather conventional blowback design with a rigidly anchored barrel and external hammer. The grip contained a conventional 20-round magazine and a rate of fire

The Czech 'Skorpion' 7.62 mm sub-machine gun; or is it a machine pistol?

reducer. For a round of 9 mm Makarov size the gun was somewhat heavy and bulky, which in turn helped stability a little during full auto fire. The gun was very nicely and expensively manufactured and this fact plus the ballistic ineffectuality probably led to its demise. A 6 gramme projectile fired at a muzzle velocity of about 340 m/sec is certainly not very impressive.

Another hybrid weapon is the Czechoslovakian vz61 sub-machine gun known by the name Scorpion. Here the official designation 'sub-machine gun' reflects its configuration and use rather accurately. A curved magazine is located in front of the trigger guard and the bolt and hammer are enclosed, the only external protruding parts being the cocking knobs. It is provided with a folding stock of bent wire. This not too bad design fires a .32 ACP round that makes it a very questionable weapon. There are two reasons for this curious choice. The first reason is that the .32 round was standardised for the Czech vz50 pistol and by Czech security forces, and the second was to obtain better controllability during full automatic fire. Military use of the mini-SMG outside the security forces, ie by the Czech Army, was limited to long-range reconnaissance units. The weapon was never used by AFV crews because the round was not standard within the Army. The vz61 SMG was licensed to Yugoslavia in the early 1980s and is used as an AFV crew weapon by the Yugoslav army. Its use by their tank crews is amply documented.

Further evolution within and outside the principal power blocs has led to a closer standardisation. The relatively slow but sustained rearmament process of Warsaw Pact countries brought nearly complete standardisation of the 9 mm Makarov round to be fired in three pistols: the Soviet PM, the Polish vz64 and the Hungarian R61 models. All these pistols have roughly the same design characteristics, being of double-action blowback design with single row magazine. Lastly came the Czechoslovakian vz82 pistol to replace the vz52 which, although a powerful gun, lacked simple design and good ergonomic features and such modern 'musts' as double action and a large capacity magazine. Therefore the brand new vz82 was developed in Czechoslovakia. This new design has all the necessary features which include double action, a two-row 12-shot magazine and ambidextrous safety and magazine catch. Its lockwork is more or less modified from that of the vz75 and very good DA/SA trigger pull is a result. Rather oddly the gun is lacquered with black paint and not blued or parkerised; a good protection against rust but not durable enough. The most interesting feature of the pistol is the use of the so-called 'polygonal rifled' hard chromed barrel and a new round to be fired through it. The round is an indigenous variant of the 9 mm Makarov, a materialised witness of the ineffectiveness of the original Russian round. It was not a very difficult task for Czech ordnance authorities to recognise that the 9 mm Makarov is not powerful enought for today's era of body armour. The new vz82 round has a 4.5 g monobloc mild steel projectile fired at 400 m/sec muzzle velocity. This improves its penetration qualities over that of the 6 g bullet at 315 m/sec of the original 9 mm Makarov, though its overall stopping power is still very questionable by Western standards. From the point of view of the future the combination of polygonal barrel and all-steel projectile are most important although not new. The cheapness of this solution should not be overlooked either. A new variant of the Scorpion mini-SMG is just being developed to fire this round; with the possible employment of a burst control device, this could advance the boundaries of that type of weapon a little further.

On the other side of the front line NATO has finally achieved full standarisation of the 9 mm Parabellum round, due to the recent adoption of the Beretta M92F pistol, chambered for this round, by the US Armed Forces. This is the significant change of the century. For many years the big .45 M1911A1 has been something like a trade mark known all over the world. The change certainly was not an easy one and there were a lot of bitter discussions and misunderstandings. In spite of extensive testing that preceded the selection there are still many objectors against the adoption. The first group of opponents proclaims that the M1911A1 is simply better than anything else. The second group states that the .45 ACP round is the best manstopper among the military pistol cartridges. The M1911A1 certainly is a very reliable weapon but on the other hand it is substantially out of fashion. A large capacity magazine, DA/SA lockwork, automatic safety and certain ambidextrous features are necessary on any recent army pistol. And last but not least, the grip safety, the flat spring extractor and the open magazine follower are surely no longer the best design.

There is hardly any soldier who would not want a lighter gun with more shots in the magazine. And when the well known fact is considered that military pistols are carried more than they are fired, any size and weight savings are even more important. The stopping power problem seems to be more important; when the .45 ACP and 9 mm Parabellum bullets are compared and nothing other is considered, the .45 is certainly the better manstopper. But when the penetration capability of 9 mm Parabellum round (so important recently) and the possibility to have more rounds in the magazine are taken into consideration, then the picture looks very different. In short, it could be said that two 8 g projectiles at 350 m/sec velocity are better than one 13 g at 250 m/sec from the military point of view. And another, this time tactical, advantage of the 9 mm

The Beretta Model 92F, adopted by the US military forces as their standard, and doubtless to be adopted by many other armies in emulation.

Parabellum round and pistol combination: 15 shots in the magazine can be far better 'traded' for space or time or better distributed among more targets than can seven shots.

The Beretta M92F that is about to be issued to the US Armed Forces is, in its slightly modified form, hardly anything more than a quite logical extension of the Beretta line of pistols; there is nothing exceptional about the design. The method of locking was more or less taken from the Walther P38 – using its tilting locking block with the unlocking pin parallel to the barrel axis. This allows the barrel to move axially in the frame; there are two advantages (rather more theoretical than practical) of such a design. The non-tilting barrel could lead to better inherent accuracy and to less inclination to stoppages due to foreign matter between a tilted barrel and the slide. Of course, the top front part of the slide is missing on the Beretta which makes clearance of stoppages easier and the insertion of single rounds directly into the chamber possible. On the other hand the slide does not protect the top of the barrel and the gun is not so muzzle heavy. It would be very instructive to know the exact conclusions of the official XM9 pistol tests in terms of mud, dust and sand reliability of the Beretta versus the SIG and other competitors. It would tell us a great deal, not only about the performance of the pistols but about the locking systems used.

To support its good name the firm of Beretta went a step further and created a variant of the M92, the 93R pistol. This is probably the most highly developed machine pistol yet seen, due to the use of the burst control device. Although not the first (there is at least one other comparable machine pistol, the VP70 of Heckler & Koch) it combines – without being too futuristic – all the advantages of a conventional pistol with some of those of the sub-machine gun. It seems to be a promising weapon but unfortunately most of the military authorities are rather too conservative to think about such designs.

There is a service, though not strictly military pistol that stands outside any thinkable categorisation: the Soviet PSM pistol. It seems to be very probable that the Soviets needed something less powerful than their 'big' 9 mm Makarov PM pistol and they wanted something using a centrefire cartridge. And at this point problems started; the only Soviet centrefire ammunition between the 9 mm Makarov and the .22 rimfire is a 7.62 mm rimmed Nagant round and its shortened, purely sporting, version. This, of course, can hardly be used in any semi-automatic pistol. That led to adoption of a very odd-looking 5.45×18 mm bottleneck round. The bore characteristics of the new PSM pistol barrel were taken from that of the AK-74 assault rifle and the new bullet

(which bears some similarity with that used in the AK-74) and cartridge case were designed. In power the new round is under any bottom limit that could be imagined. Its tiny 2.6 g projectile is fired at 315 m/sec muzzle velocity. The PSM pistol is a conventionally designed DA/SA blowback with an 8-round magazine. All possible design effort was spent to make the pistol as flat as possible.[2] This shows that the concealability of the weapon was the most preferred requirement of the basic specification. According to the known information the gun is intended for security personnel, including the security network of the Soviet Army. Nevertheless, one can easily imagine it in the hand of a Communist party functionary and in another use where any possible opponent is unarmed.

It is a matter of interest that in spite of the fact that a basic pistol ammunition standardisation within the main blocs was achieved (9 mm Parabellum for NATO and 9 mm Makarov for the Warsaw Pact) the area on the whole is still very colourful, though not so important as the very sensitive area of rifle ammunition where, by the way, the 5.56 NATO round and the 5.45×39 Soviet round are relatively closer to one another than 9 mm Parabellum and the 9 mm Makarov. This in no case means that controversies are less sharp or less frequent.

Now that the dust around the pistols of the two main blocs has settled down and the picture shows us that both the blocs are rather conservative it is interesting to take a look at other nations. Without any doubt the most interesting pistol is the Austrian Glock 17. It is a 17-shot pistol with lockwork which is difficult to define: something of a combination of striker-fired and purely DA pistol with internal hammer. The most interesting feature is its full plastic frame with the metal parts moulded into it. The Austrians seem to have good experience of plastic construction with their AUG rifle that led to their adoption of the Glock. Surprisingly, plastics were employed to create main sub-assemblies of firearms before they were used in construction of standard small arms ammunition.

It seems rather probable that the design of pistols as well as of pistol ammunition will not be stagnant and even outsiders can contribute to overall progress. Though any prognostication is of very limited value – as has been many times proven – we can expect a broader use of plastic and further development of armour piercing pistol ammunition because of the wide use of body armour.

[2] Even the safety lever employed in the design is inspired by that of the Mauser C/96 which protrudes back rather than to the side!

The Rising Cost of Warfare

Ian V. Hogg

The most difficult figure to extract from an armaments manufacturer is not the muzzle velocity, or the weight, or the mean time between failures of his product; it is the price. In many ways this is understandable, because a lot of odd factors creep into the business of assessing a price. How difficult is it going to be to get the money out of the customer? How many does he want – like everything else, weapons come cheaper by the dozen. Does he want a spares and maintenance back-up which will bring in a steady income and could be worth a discount off the weapons? Is there an 'offset' deal – you buy our missiles, we buy your armoured cars?

Nevertheless, with some careful reading of published contracts, study of the market, and the use of a good-quality crystal ball, one can come to some reasonable estimates. And the more one does so, the more one becomes convinced that the great deterrent of the 21st century is not going to be a space weapon, but simply the cost of going to war; nobody is going to be able to afford it.

I can still recall the shock felt by the man in the street when somebody, in 1944, revealed that the Second World War was costing Britain the staggering sum of £12 million per day. Looked at from the viewpoint of 1985 this seems to be a reasonable bargain; we had, after all, some 4,683,000 men and women under arms around the world, 14 armoured divisions, 30 infantry divisions, and a massive services backup. But the most revealing statistics are the actual costs of the weapons with which these troops were armed.

Some time ago I came across a German document showing the prices of the standard weapons used by the Third Reich, and the figures were, frankly, incredible. The Walther P38 pistol, for example, was supplied to the German Army at a contract price of 32 Reichmarks – £2.77 at the 1939 rate of exchange. You cannot even buy a plastic model of one for that price today. The Mauser Kar 98K rifle was £6.06, and the MG42 machine gun £21.64. The 88 mm Flak gun came in at £2,900 and the

Tiger tank cost a fearsome £21,700. By comparison the current Walther P5 retails on the commercial market for just over £400, the Heckler & Koch G3, which might be considered today's equivalent of the Kar 98K, for about the same, and any of the newest battle tanks is in excess of £1 million.

The obvious and quick response to this is to say 'Inflation', but that isn't the only cause; inflation means, speaking broadly, that today's price for anything is about 25 times the price in 1939, and by that reckoning the Walther pistol ought to cost about £70 and the main battle tank half-a-million pounds. Built into today's prices is an additional element which pays for the research and development department, the advanced technology, the computerised machine tools, and doubtless the bad debts of some of the worse credit risks.

But the whole fearsome panorama is revealed when we take a combat formation, calculate what it cost to arm it and supply it for 24 hours of battle in 1944, and then do the same sum for the same formation today. Let us take an armoured division as our example, and stick to the armament costs; ignore the pay, the uniforms, and the food.

Since we happen to have accurate and ample figures for German weapons, let us take the 1944 Panzer division. It consisted of 471 officers and 13,255 men; was armed with 51 Panther and 52 PzKpfw IV battle tanks, 60 assorted pieces of field artillery, eight 88 mm anti-aircraft guns, 47 75 mm anti-tank guns, 74 20 mm air defence guns, 64 machine guns, 1543 sub-machine guns, 3,317 pistols and 9,186 rifles. There were also flamethrowers, mortars and soft vehicles, but we will leave these out in order to keep things simple.

51 Panther tanks at £10,138	£517,038
52 PzKpfw IV tanks at £8957	465,764
47 75 mm SP anti-tank guns at £5600	263,200
60 pieces of artillery, varying costs,	269,784
8 × 88 mm Flak 36 guns at £2909	23,272
47 75 mm PAK 40 guns at £1038	48,786

74 20 mm Flak 38 at £562	41,588
64 MG42 at £21.64	1,385
1543 MP40 at £5.19	8,008
3,317 Pistole '38 at £2.77	9,188
9186 Mauser Kar 98K at £6.06	55,667
TOTAL	£1,703,680

Having mustered all this on to the battlefield, it then has to fight, and to do this it required ammunition. Detailing and costing the 'day of fire' allocations would take far too much space here, so we will simply assume that every weapon needed 100 rounds of ammunition to fight for one day and that this all adds up to a further £314,400. So that to put the Panzer division into the field and fight for one day cost just over two million pounds in 1944.

Now let us look at an equivalent 1985 formation, the British armoured division; we need to make some comparative adjustments, since there are no longer any anti-tank guns nor any medium anti-aircraft guns, missiles having replaced them. No allowance is being made for the provision of night vision equipment, modern radio equipment, surveillance radars, helicopters and similar technological necessities. But we are still looking at the cost of putting an armoured division into the field and operating it for one day. Some of the figures are approximations; the precise number of vehicles seems to be a moveable feast, and not all the costs have been published in detail.

148 main battle tanks at £850,000	£125,800,000
75 reconnaissance tanks at £400,000	30,000,000
24 SP 105 mm guns at £210,000	5,040,000
12 SP 155 mm howitzers at £385,000	4,620,000
6 SP 8 in howitzers at £402,000	2,412,000
130 APCs at £55,000	7,150,000
20 SP Swingfire launchers at £100,000	2,000,000
32 Milan launchers at £35,000	1,120,000
25 Blowpipe launchers at £22,000	550,000
4 Tracked Rapier launchers	4,000,000
300 machine guns at £750	225,000
700 pistols at £100	70,000
2000 sub-machine guns at £200	400,000
8000 rifles at £250	2,000,000
TOTAL	£185,387,000

And for the ammunition, on the same basis as before but allowing only 15 missiles per launcher, a further £22,293,500, to give a grand total of £207,680,500, slightly over 102 times the cost in 1944.

This, you may think, is bad enough; but working on the (reasonable) assumption that NATO divisions are much the same and NATO costs are similar, if we now multiply that figure by the number of armoured divisions in NATO, and add on another calculated sum representing the infantry and other divisions we reach a total of £4,620 million. And note that this is purely the 'teeth' arms; the prospect of calculating the capital expenditure and running costs of the administrative tail would daunt a Senior Wrangler.

And having put up four milliard pounds to get the troops in place and stock them for one day, the taxpayers will then be called on to keep them going to the tune of about £528 million *per day* for ammunition. Plus pay, clothing, rations and the day-to-day running of the administrative tail aforesaid. And we haven't even thought about the air and naval forces. Or the nuclear deterrent. One way and another, it looks as if a major war is going to cost NATO £1000 million a day to run in the future. The only consolation is that, based on the same sort of figures, it is going to cost the Warsaw Pact forces about £2500 million a day; and if we take the best figures for the Warsaw Pact GNP it gives a figure of £1575 million per day, so they have a one milliard deficit. By contrast the GNP of the NATO countries who have forces in Germany is some £2,769 million per day, which leaves them some loose change for feeding their civil populations and other necessary expenses.

Such a comparison, entertaining though it may be, is of course invalid, since the methods of costing employed in the Warsaw Pact bear no resemblance to the methods used in the West. Moreover the Warsaw Pact population is accustomed to rather less luxury in its day-to-day living than obtains in the West and would be less inclined to rebel if the standard was cut even further in the interest of facilitating armament production. Guns before butter, as somebody once said. But even so, there is food for thought in these figures, notwithstanding, as I said, that they are an approximation.

Around the Exhibitions

1985, an odd-numbered year, was a year for the Paris Air Show and the French Army Exhibition Satory X since these alternate with the British Army Equipment Exhibition and Farnborough Air Show in even-numbered years. In addition there was the annual US Army Association convention and show in Washington and the second Milipol, a newly-established annual display of police and internal security equipment held in Paris. None produced anything revolutionary, but they all had something of interest.

Typical of the current gun/missile mix which is being vigorously promoted as a short-range air defence solution was this combination of the British Blowpipe missile and the American Gatling-type cannon mounted on an armoured car. (*Paris Air Show*)

Above left: **Oerlikon's Escorter 35 air defence equipment mounts two 35 mm cannon on an unusual wheeled chassis with exceptional cross-country performance.** (*Paris Air Show*)

Above: **Training and simulation is a growth industry, particularly as service equipments become more complicated to use and maintain. This is the dummy French 155 mm TR howitzer designed to teach men the loading and firing drills without the expense of live ammunition.** (*Satory*)

Left: **A French Sagaie 90 wheeled reconnaissance vehicle with its basic load of ammunition.** (*Satory*)

Overleaf

Top left: **The GIAT Alfac anti-tank rocket launcher, one of the many designs which have appeared in the past few years.** (*Satory*)

Top right: **One of the useful features of military exhibitions is that visiting soldiers can get their hands on equipment before it reaches them through the channels of issue. A US soldier checks out the British 81 mm mortar; this has been adopted by the US forces but it will probably be some time before he will see it in his unit.** (*AUSA, Washington*)

Below left: **The new 105 mm French light gun on display in the USA. This, and similar lightweight weapons, have revived interest in the concept of anti-tank artillery.** (*AUSA*)

Below right: **Protect me, protect my dog. If policemen can have bullet-proof vests, why not police dogs?** (*Milipol, Paris*)

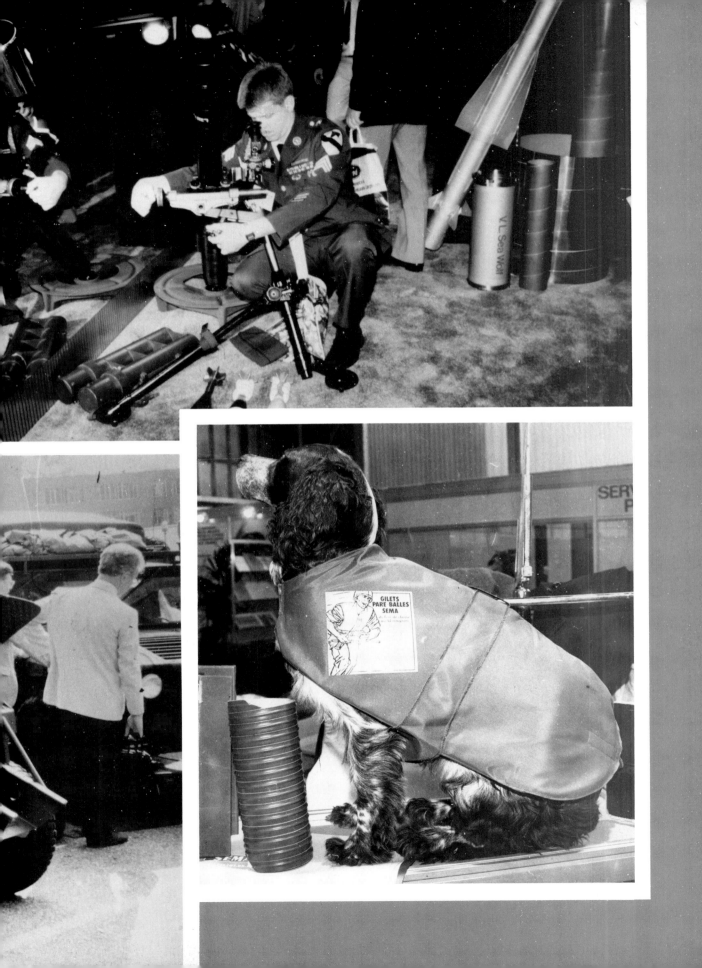

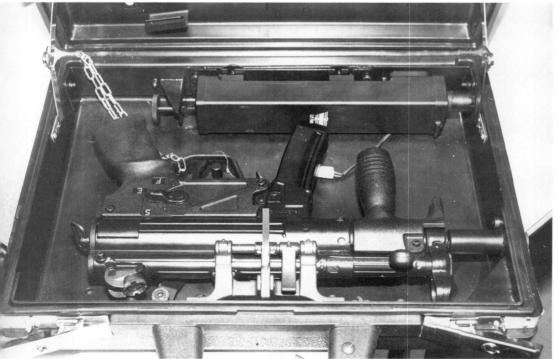

Above: **The British police theory of 'minimum force' finds few adherents elsewhere. The Panhard Vehicule Blinde Legere M11 originally appeared as a military armoured car; here it is shown as a potential police car. (*Milipol*)**

Left: **For the undercover operator or bodyguard, this briefcase contains a Heckler & Koch MP5K sub-machine gun and a laser spot aiming indicator. A button in the handle switches on the laser spot, the case holder then guides it to his target, and a trigger in the handle allows the gun to be fired. (*Milipol*)**

Current and Future American Light Tank Developments

Christopher F. Foss

Although the United States Army currently has less than 100 light tanks in front-line service there has recently been a resurgence of interest in this type of vehicle for use by the new light divisions being formed for rapid overseas deployment by air. This article looks not only at the new light tanks being offered to the United States Army but also older United States tanks, some of which are over 40 years old, still giving useful service in some parts of the world.

The Bernardini company of Brazil has rebuilt 80 old Stuart light tanks for the Brazilian Army. These are designated the X1A1 and have many improvements including a diesel engine and 90 mm gun.

Second World War Light Tank Production

During the Second World War the United States Army made extensive use of light tanks, not only in the traditional role of reconnaissance, but also in place of the heavier and better armoured Sherman medium tanks in difficult terrain such as that encountered in the Far East.

Light tank production in the United States during the Second World War amounted to 13,859 M3s, 8884 M5s and 4070 M24 Chaffees. Many of these light tanks were supplied to the Allies during this conflict, with the M3, or General Stuart, being supplied in large numbers to the British Army for use in the Western Desert where it

soon became known as the Honey because of its excellent reliability.

Post-war Military Aid Programme

At the end of the Second World War the United States was left with massive quantities of every conceivable type of military equipment including large numbers of light tanks which were supplied to many countries in the Far East, Central and South America under the Military Aid Programme.

In 1985 the M3 still remains in service with Brazil, Chile, Colombia, Ecuador, Guatemala, Mexico and

Modernised M24 Chaffee light tank of the Norwegian Army fitted with new diesel engine and French 90 mm DEFA gun. These vehicles are designated the NM-116 and have recently been fitted with a laser rangefinder to improve gun accuracy.

M24 Chaffee

The M24 Chaffee light tank was supplied to many countries after the end of the Second World War including Austria, Cambodia, Ethiopia, France, Greece, Iran, Iraq, Japan, Laos, Norway, Pakistan, Portugal, Philippines, Saudi Arabia, Spain, Taiwan, Thailand, Turkey, Uruguay and Vietnam, and remains in service with many of these countries even to this day. The M24 Chaffee has seen post-war combat with a number of countries including France (in Indo-China and elsewhere), Laos, Pakistan and Vietnam.

Between 1975 and 1976 Thune-Eureka of Norway rebuilt 54 M24 tanks with new engine and transmission, French 90 mm (3.54-in) gun replacing original 75 mm (2.95-inch) weapon, 7.62 mm (0.30) coaxial machine gun replaced by 12.7 mm (0.50-inch) machine gun and bow machine gun removed so that additional ammunition can be carried, Simrad laser rangefinder installed for greater accuracy and new smoke dischargers.

These modernised M24 Chaffees are known as NM-116s and are still in service with the Norwegian Army.

The American company of NAPCO also markets this retrofit package and is believed to have sold a quantity of these to Taiwan for its M24 Chaffee light tanks. These still retain their original 75 mm (2.95-inch) guns.

M41 Walker Bulldog Light Tank

The M24 Chaffee light tank was replaced in the United States Army by the M41, commonly known as the Walker Bulldog. About 5500 of these were built from 1951 by the Cadillac Motor Car Division of General Motors Corporation at the Cleveland Tank Arsenal in Ohio.

In 1985 the M41 remains in service with Brazil, Chile, Denmark, Ethiopia, Greece, Japan, Philippines, Spain, Taiwan, Thailand, Tunisia, Turkey, Sudan, Uruguay and Vietnam, although the serviceability of the latter must now be in some doubt.

The M41 light tank has excellent cross-country mobility and is armed with a 76 mm (2.99-inch) gun firing a wide range of ammunition, 7.62 mm (0.30-inch) coaxial and 12.7 mm (0.50-inch) anti-aircraft machine guns.

The main drawback of the M41 has always been its petrol engine which is very thirsty on fuel and gives the tank an operational range of just 161 km (100 miles) totally inadequate by todays standards. In recent years a number of companies including Bernardini of Brazil, NAPCO of the United States, Talbot of Spain, Levy of Canada and FFG of West Germany, have all developed diesel repower packages for the M41 which offer a significant increase in operating range as well as reduced risk of fire.

Paraguay, while Mexico uses the M5 and its M8 self-propelled howitzer counterpart and Haiti uses both the M3A1 and M5A1.

The Bernardini company of São Paulo, Brazil, has in recent years, been modernising old M3 Stuart light tanks to extend their lives for a few more years. The X1A1, of which 80 have been rebuilt, has a 90 mm (3.54-inch) gun, new fire control system, modernised suspension, new diesel engine for longer range and so on. Further development resulted in the X1A2 which was built from scratch and 30 of these have been produced for the Brazilian Army. This model is also being offered for export.

Brazil has already modernised well over 250 of its M41 tanks and in 1985 Denmark decided to repower its M41 with a Cummins engine.

Other companies are offering new fire control systems and night vision equipment for the M41 while AAI of the United States have developed a new 76 mm Armour Piercing Fin Stabilised Discarding Sabot (ASPFSDS) round with greatly increased armour piercing capabilities. This round has already been adopted by Denmark for its M41 light tanks.

The Belgian company of Cockerill have developed a modernisation package for the M41 using their 90 mm (3.54-inch) Mk IV gun which can fire a wide range of ammunition including HEAT-T, HESH-T, APFSDS-T, HE-APERS-T and Smoke-WP-T. This package has already been sold to Uruguay for its M41 light tanks.

M41 Replaced in US Army by M551

In the United States Army the M41 Walker Bulldog light tank was replaced by the M551 Sheridan light tank, although its correct designation is an Armoured Reconnaissance/Airborne Assault Vehicle or AR/AAV for short.

A total of 1700 vehicles were built between 1966 and 1970 by the Allison Division of the General motors Corporation at the Cleveland Tank-Automotive Plant. The M551 was evaluated by a number of countries but no export sales were achieved. The M551 saw some

Above: **M41 light tank with original 76 mm gun replaced by the much more potent Cockerill 90 mm Mk IV. This version has already been sold to Uruguay.**

Below: **M41B light tank of the Brazilian Army which not only has a more powerful diesel engine but a 90 mm gun which fires the same ammunition as the ENGESA EE-9 Cascavel armoured cars of the Brazilian Army.**

Above: **M41 light tank modernised by Talbot of Spain which has a number of improvements including a diesel engine in place of the very inefficient petrol engine.**

This Cazador tank destroyer has been developed by Talbot of Spain and consists of a modernised M41 light tank chassis fitted with the Emerson TOW Under Armor twin ATGW launcher. Photo is from rear with launcher elevated and traversed to rear.

action in South Vietnam but there were problems with its weapon system and its thin hull gave little protection against the ever increasing threat of mines.

The M551 is armed with a 152 mm (6-inch) weapon that can fire the Shillelagh missile with a HEAT (High Explosive Anti-Tank) warhead or a number of conventional rounds with a combustible cartridge case.

In 1978 it was announced that the M551 was to be phased out of service with the United States Army and its role taken over by M60A1 Main Battle Tanks. By 1985 the M551 was only in front-line service with one battalion attached to the 82nd Airborne Division although over 300 M551s are used by the National Training Centre at Fort Irwin in California where they

have been modified externally to resemble Soviet armoured vehicles such as the T-72 MBT, BMP mechanised infantry combat vehicle, ZSU-23-4 self-propelled anti-aircraft gun system, BMD airborne combat vehicle and the 122 mm (4.8-inch) 2S1 self-propelled howitzer.

ACVT Programme

In the mid-1970s the United States built two experimental armoured vehicles under the Armored Combat Vehicle Technology (ACVT) Programme, these were the Highly Mobility Test Vehicle (HIMAG) and the High Survivability Test Vehicle (Lightweight) (HSTV(L)), the latter being designed and built by AAI.

HIMAG was the heavier of the two vehicles and its weight could be varied between 30, 392 and 39, 766 kg (67,000 lb to 87,668 lb) and its engine output between 1000 hp (745 kW) to 1500 hp (1118 kW) so enabling a

Above: **Some 1700 M551 Sheridan tanks were built for the United States Army but now remain in front line service with just one battalion attached to the 82nd Airborne Division.**

Below: **M551 modified to resemble a Soviet armoured vehicle for use at the United States Army's National Training Centre at Fort Irwin, California.** (*Michael Green/US Army*)

The High Survivability Test Vehicle (Lightweight) which like the HIMAG was built as part of the Armored Combat Vehicle Technology programme in the mid-1970s. Both of these were research vehicles and were not placed in production.

The experimental High Survivability Test Vehicle (Lightweight) from rear showing 75 mm ARES automatic cannon. (US Army)

wide range of power-to-weight ratios to be obtained. Main armament comprised an ARES 75 mm automatic gun with a Deleco Electronics Division fire control system.

The HSTV(L) was a much lighter vehicle weighing 20,450 kg (45,022 lb) and armed with an ARES 75 mm cannon, 7.62 mm (0.30-inch) coaxial machine gun and a similar weapon on the turret roof. A Texas Instruments hunter-killer fire control system was installed with both day and night capability. The Avco Lycoming 650 gas turbine engine developed 650 hp (485 kW) and gave the vehicle a power-to-weight ratio of 32 hp (24 kW) per tonne, far in advance of any MBT in service today.

The HIMAG and HSTV(L) were research vehicles to investigate new concepts in fire control systems, the rapid-fire 75 mm ARES gun and high power-to-weight ratios.

AAI Build Light Tank

Many years ago AAI built a prototype of a light tank for the United States Army called the T92. This was armed with a 76 mm (3-inch) gun in a cleft turret with one 7.62 mm (0.30-inch) and one 12.7 mm (0.50-inch) machine gun mounted in individual cupolas either side of the main armament. The T92 had a three-man crew and was powered by a Continental petrol engine coupled to an Allison transmission. The T92 was not however placed in production.

The experimental T92 light tank built for the US Army by AAI. This featured a 76 mm gun in a cleft turret but it was not placed in production.

AAI light tank with two man turret armed with same 76 mm
gun as installed in the old M41 light tank but firing new AAI
developed armour piercing fin stabilised discarding sabot
ammunition. This tank has already been demonstrated in
Venezuela in 1984 with good results.

Based on their experience in building the HSTV(L) for the United States Army AAI started private venture development work on a new light tank which was finally unveilled in 1980 as the Rapid Deployment Force/Light Tank.

This has been designed for rapid transport by aircraft or helicopter to exactly where it is needed. A Lockheed C-5B can carry eight RDF/LT while the Marine Corps CH-53E helicopter can carry one RDF/LT.

Main armament comprises an ARES 75 mm automatic cannon with a 7.62 mm (0.50) coaxial machine gun and a similar weapon on the turret roof for anti-aircraft defence. The vehicle is powered by the Detroit Diesel 6V-53T engine developing 350 hp (261 kW)

which is already in the United States Army inventory, coupled to an Allison X-200 automatic transmission.

So far however this vehicle has not been adopted by the United States Army or any other army. In October 1985 the RDF/LT was shown fitted with four surface-to-air missiles, two either side of the main armament, to give additional air defence capability.

At present the ARES 75 mm (2.95-inch) gun has not completed its development so is not available for export. For the export market AAI have built the 13.2-tonne Rapid Deployment Force Light Tank which has a similiar chassis but a new two man turret armed with the same 76 mm (2.99-inch) gun as the M41 which also fires the new AAI developed Armour Piercing Fin Stabilised Discarding Sabot (APFSDS) round. This version of the RDF/LT has already been tested in Venezuela.

Prototype of the private venture AAI Rapid Deployment Force Light Tank armed with 75 mm ARES automatic cannon mounted externally.

Latest version of AAI Rapid Deployment Force Light Tank with new turret but still armed with 75 mm ARES automatic cannon, French SFIM roof mounted sight and additional applique armour on the hull sides.

MPGS and MPWS Programmes

For some years the United States Marine Corps has had a requirement for a Mobile Protected Weapons System (MPWS) while the Army has a requirement for a Mobile Protected Gun System (MPGS).

In 1981 the Marine Corps did issue contracts for both hybrid and conceptual approaches for the MPWS requirement but in the end these were not proceeded with. In 1981 the Marine Corps agreed to merge its requirements with those of the Army as their requirements are almost identical. The major difference between the two were that the Marines want the vehicle capable of being lifted by the CH-53E helicopter whereas the Army does not have this requirement so its vehicle would be a bit heavier and have improved armour protection.

The MPGS was later known as the Close Assault Weapon System (CLAWS) or more recently the Armored Gun System (AGS) but as of November 1985 no request for proposals had gone out to industry for a variety of factors including lack of funding. The Armored Gun System is urgently needed by the Marine Corps and the Army, the latter for its new light divisions whose only ground based anti-tank weapons at present are the TOW system installed on 4 × 4 cross-country vehicles.

The United States Army have released outline requirements for the Armored Gun System. These include a weight of 19 to 21 US tons, three-man crew, 105 mm gun with automatic loader, 7.62 mm (0.30-inch) coaxial and 7.62 mm (0.30-inch) anti-aircraft machine guns, stabilised sights for commander and gunner, good power-to-weight ratio and cross-country mobility, and a NBC system.

Prototypes Built with Company Funding

Although no formal request for proposals have yet been released by the United States Army at least three companies have already invested considerable funds in building prototypes of new light tanks which could meet the requirements of the United States Army, or indeed, the export market.

Cadillac Gage Stingray

Since the early 1960s the Cadillac Gage company has been engaged in the design and development of the Commando range fo 4 × 4 multi-mission vehicles of which over 4000 have been built for the home and export markets. More recently the company has designed the V-300 (6 × 6), Commando Ranger (4 × 4) and Commando Scout (4 × 4) vehicles.

Some years ago the company noted that many countries wanted a light tracked tank that would have

Cadillac Gage Stingray light tank armed with a British Royal Ordnance 105 mm low recoil gun was unveiled in late 1984 and has been designed to meet requirements of both home and export markets.

the mobility and fire power of a MBT but weigh less and be easier to maintain and operate.

With these requirements in mind Cadillac Gage designed and built the Stingray light tank which was shown in public for the first time in October 1984.

Stingray has a four-man crew consisting of commander, gunner, loader and driver and is armed with the British Royal Ordnance 105 mm low recoil gun fitted with a thermal sleeve, fume extractor and a muzzle brake. This can fire all standard 105 mm NATO ammunition including that used in the American M60 and M1 tanks. A 7.62 mm machine gun is mounted coaxial with the main armament and a 7.62 mm or

12.7 mm machine gun can be mounted on the turret roof for anti-aircraft defence.

Stingray has the British Marconi Command and Control Systems Digital Fire Control System that allows both stationary and moving targets to be engaged with a high probability of first round hit while the Stingray itself is stationary or moving.

Turret traverse and weapon elevation is electro-hydraulic with Cadillac Gage, Control Systems Division, commander's and gunner's controls.

Stingray is powered by a Detroit Diesel Model 8V-92 TA diesel developing 525 hp (391 kW) at 2300 rpm coupled to a fully automatic transmission. With a combat weight of 19,051 kg (42,000 lb), Stingray has a power-to-weight ratio of 28.24 hp/tonne.

The steel armour of Stingray provides protection against Soviet 14.5 mm KPVT armour-piercing rounds over the frontal arc and against 7.62 mm armour piercing rounds over the remainder of the vehicle. If required applique armour can be provided for increased armour protection.

So far two prototypes of the Stingray have been built. In designing Stingray Cadillac Gage have an eye on both the home and export markets, although the former at present seems to have a preference to a two-man turret with an automatic loader.

The private venture FMC Ordnance Division Close Combat Vehicle (Light) was unveiled in October 1985 and features a three man crew and a 105 mm gun fed by an automatic loader which enables a rate of fire of 12 rounds a minute to be achieved.

FMC CCV-L

The Defense Systems Group of the FMC Corporation based at San Jose in California is the largest manufacturer of tracked vehicles in the world and is currently producing M113 series vehicles for both the home and export markets, M2 Bradley infantry fighting vehicles and M3 cavalry fighting vehicles for the United States Army and LVTP7A1 amphibious assault vehicles for the United States Marine Corps.

In October 1985 FMC Corporation unveiled its private venture Close Combat Vehicle – Light (CCV-L) which it started developing in 1983.

The CCV-L has the driver at the front, two-man turret in the centre and engine and transmission at the rear.

The commander and gunner are seated on the right of the turret with the automatic loader being installed in the left side of the turret. Main armament comprises 105 mm gun with a Rheinmetall recoil system and is fed from an automatic loader designed by FMC Northern Ordnance Division who has some 40 years experience in the design and development of automatic loading systems. A total of 19 rounds of 105 mm ammunition are carried in the automatic loader for ready use with a further 24 rounds being stored in the front part of the hull. The automatic loader enables 12 rounds to be fired a minute. A 7.62 mm machine gun with 5000 rounds carried its mounted coaxial with the main armament, and a Tracor MBA advanced countermeasures system is mounted either side of turret and fires smoke or screening grenades.

The gunner has a day/night two-axis stabilised sight while commander has an independent thermal viewer which also is two-axis stabilised. Fire computer is based on that installed in the M1 MBT while gun and turret drives are also based on those in the M1 MBT.

The CCV-L is powered by a Detroit-Diesel Model 6V-92TA developing 552 hp at 2400 rpm coupled to an General Electric HMPT-500-3 fully automatic transmission which is already used in the M2/M3 armoured vehicles in service with the US Army.

The prototype of the CCV-L was rolled out in August 1985. After initial gunnery and automotive trials it was airlifted to Washington in a commercial C-130 Hercules transport aircraft and then shown for the first time at the 1985 Association of the United States Army meeting. By late 1985 a total of $25 million had been spent by FMC on the CCV-L project. Of this sum about $16 million came from within the company and the remainder from sub-component supplies such as Rheinmetall, Cadillac Gage, Detroit Diesel, General Electric and Hughes Aircraft.

Teledyne Armored Gun System

The General Products Division of Teledyne Continental Motors have been supplying diesel engines to the United States Army for many years but more recently has become involved in providing retrofit packages for armoured vehicles such as the Centurion and AMX-30 MBTs.

In 1982 the company started concept work on a light tracked combat vehicle which could meet future United States Army requirements. The prototype of this, now called the Teledyne Armored Gun System, ran for the first time, without its armament in late 1983.

Prototype of the Teledyne Continental Motors Armored Gun System which is unique in that the 105 mm gun is mounted externally with the three man crew consisting of commander, gunner and driver are within safety of the hull.

So far the vehicle has not been shown in public although it was demonstrated at Fort Knox early in 1985.

The Teledyne AGS has a number of unusual features including a front-mounted powerpack that uses the same engine and transmission as that installed in the M2 Bradley infantry fighting vehicles of the United States Army. The driver is seated to the rear of the engine on the left and to the rear of the driver is a pedestal mounted 105 mm M68 gun fed from an automatic loader with 29 rounds of ready use ammunition which enables a firing rate of 10 to 12 rounds a minute. The 105 mm gun fires all standard 105 mm ammunition already in the United States Army inventory for the M60 series and M1 MBT. A 7.62 mm machine gun is mounted coaxial with the 105 mm gun and a similiar weapon can be externally mounted on the hull roof for local and anti-aircraft defence. A key advantage of the externally mounted gun is that all of the crew are contained within the safety of the hull armour.

The gunner is seated forward of the gun on the left with the commander to his right. The gunner has a primary day/night sight with remote video link for vehicle commander who also has periscopes for all round observation.

Suspension is of the hydropneumatic type which gives excellent mobility across country as well as providing a more stable gun platform.

Other features of the Teledyne AGS include a fire suppression system, excellent armour protection and the ability to add other weapons such as TOW or Hellfire missiles either side of the 105 mm gun pod. The chassis of the vehicle could also be used for a wide range of other purposes including air defence, anti-tank (long range), infantry fighting vehicle, command post and mortar carrier, to name but a few. It is also possible, according to Teledyne, to replace the 105 mm gun by a 120 mm weapon.

Conclusion

As mentioned above there are at least three United States companies offering tracked vehicles to meet the future AGS requirement, Cadillac Gage, FMC and Teledyne Continental Motors. There are also a number of overseas countries who could offer vehicles to meet this requirement, include GIAT with the AMX-1ORC (6 × 6) armoured car and Hagglunds and Soner of Sweden with their Ikv-91/105 light tank which is already at the prototype stage.

The United States Army needs a new light tank but this can only be provided if Congress allocate the required funding, which they have so far failed to do. It is hoped that reason will prevail and that some funding will at the very least be made to provide prototype vehicles for trials before production commences.

New Equipment

Meeting customers' demands, the world's designers have applied their minds to small arms and close-quarter weapons in 1985. The American Army are searching for their next-generation rifle, the Italians for a new assault rifle, everyone for close-range weapons of greater destructiveness. We present our usual selection of this year's offerings.

The AAI Corporation of the USA is developing this 'Advanced Combat Rifle', firing a caseless cartridge, for consideration as the US Army's next generation of rifle. The ACR is fitted with a rangefinding optical sight and fires a full-calibre 5.56 mm bullet or a sabot 4.32 mm bullet.

A British development for internal security forces, the Hilton Multi-purpose Riot Gun. By interchanging barrels on the basic mechanism, it can be put together as a 37 mm riot gun, a 26 mm signal gun, a 12-bore shotgun or a 5.56 mm rifle.

Power in a suitcase. The Spanish Ameli 5.56 mm light machine gun packed into its carrying case. It is said that the British Special Air Service have shown considerable interest in this potent little weapon.

The Beretta AS 70/90 5.56 mm light machine gun, the other half of the new Beretta family; this, though, is not being offered to the Italian Army but is intended for export.

Above: **Big Brother is watching you. This turret unit, developed by Fabrique Nationale, Herstal, carries a TV camera and two 7.62 mm machine guns. Numbers can be mast-mounted around the perimeter of security areas and linked to a central control room. The TV camera pictures are sampled by computer; should an intruder appear the computer alerts an operator who can then review the picture and, if an intruder has appeared, can warn him by means of a loudspeaker in the turret or, if this fails, open up with the machine guns.**

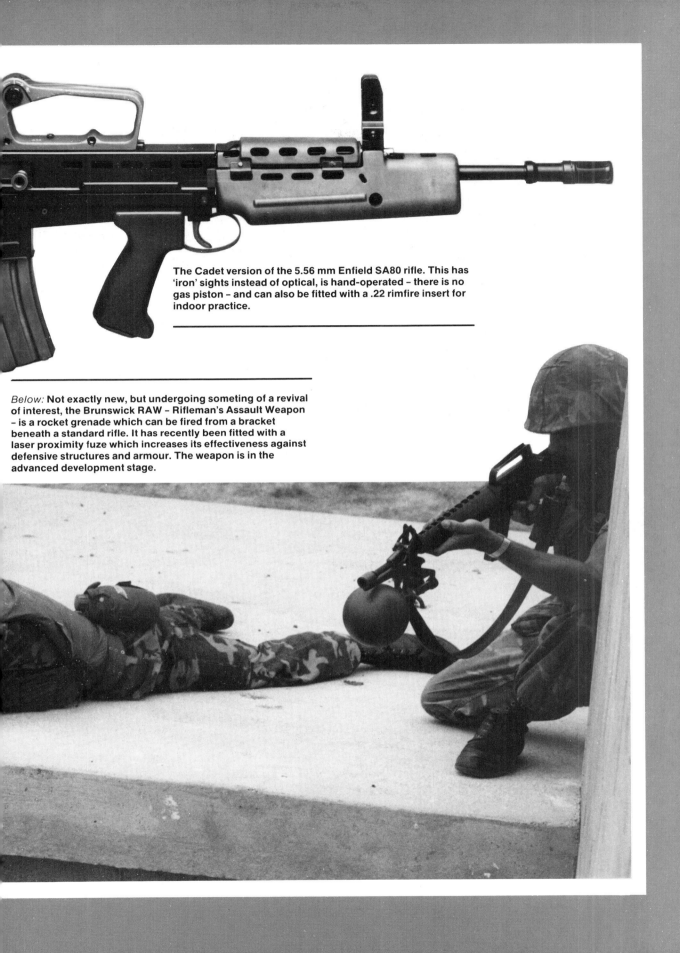

The Cadet version of the 5.56 mm Enfield SA80 rifle. This has 'iron' sights instead of optical, is hand-operated – there is no gas piston – and can also be fitted with a .22 rimfire insert for indoor practice.

Below: Not exactly new, but undergoing someting of a revival of interest, the Brunswick RAW – Rifleman's Assault Weapon – is a rocket grenade which can be fired from a bracket beneath a standard rifle. It has recently been fitted with a laser proximity fuze which increases its effectiveness against defensive structures and armour. The weapon is in the advanced development stage.

Below: The Beretta 5.56 mm 70/90 assault rifle, together with its bayonet and bipod. This has been designed to meet an Italian Army requirement for a new 5.56 mm small arms family.

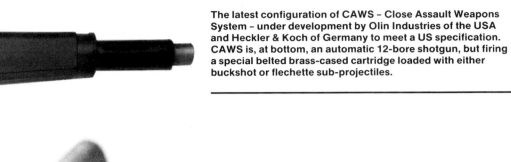

The latest configuration of CAWS – Close Assault Weapons System – under development by Olin Industries of the USA and Heckler & Koch of Germany to meet a US specification. CAWS is, at bottom, an automatic 12-bore shotgun, but firing a special belted brass-cased cartridge loaded with either buckshot or flechette sub-projectiles.

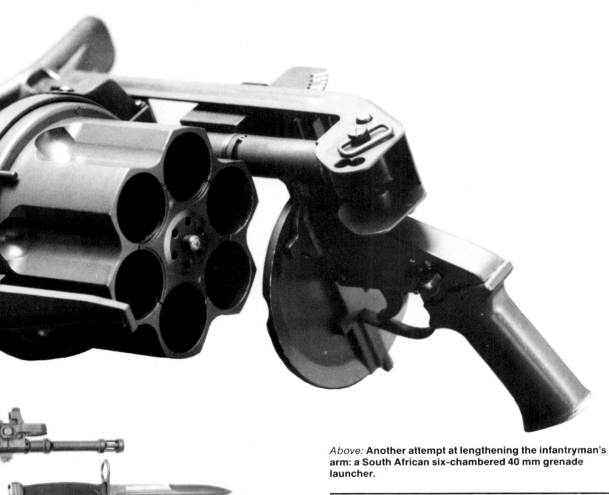

Above: **Another attempt at lengthening the infantryman's arm: a South African six-chambered 40 mm grenade launcher.**

Well, it makes a change. Luigi Franchi of Italy, hitherto best known as a maker of shotguns, has gone into the revolver business with this RF83 revolver. It comes in a variety of models, this being the Super Target in .38 Special calibre.

Below: Fabrique Nationale, Herstal, of Belgium, have developed the BRG-15 15 mm heavy machine gun (*right*) to supplant the .50 Browning (*left*) in the future. The BRG-15 has dual feed and a powerful cartridge which can drive its bullet through both sides of most light armoured vehicles at a mile range.

The Regimental System and Combat Motivation

Anthony Kellett

Saving the colours of the 1st Battalion, 24th Regiment South Wales Borderers, at Isandhlwana in 1879.

The loving cup of the 14th/20th Hussars – 'The Emperor'.
(Photo by Michael Clarke in *Officer's Mess: Life and Customs in the Regiments* by Lt Col R.J. Dickinson/Midas Books).

The 'regimental system' is frequently invoked, but rarely analyzed. As one British officer explained, it is regarded as 'a given', being generally well-understood by those with close experience of it. Yet a series of recent interviews in a Canadian infantry battalion produced almost as many explanations of the system as there were interviewees. But any attempt to study the regimental system is likely to evoke suspicion. As a former British regimental medical officer put it, the regimental system is 'one of the most sacred of our Army's "sacred cows"'.[1]

The present seems an appropriate time to study the regimental system. In the quarter-century after the Second World War, British and Canadian regiments were confronted with regular and sometimes drastic changes. But the past fifteen years have been a period of stability for them, and the cycle of change appears to have stopped. In the United States, concern at apparent problems of cohesion among combat units in Vietnam led at the beginning of the 1980s to the introduction of a new manning programme, which included the adoption of many facets of the Commonwealth-style regimental

in his study of a regular battalion at that time, Baynes [2] contended that this spirit would probably never again mean as much as it did to the regular of 1914. A major reorganisation of the infantry in 1946-48 demolished the Cardwell system by reducing almost all regiments to single battalions, and other reforms followed. Nonetheless, regiments have adapted successfully to these changes, and the regimental system remains a central feature of the British Army.

Up to the mid-1960s the Canadian Army largely modelled itself on the British in dress, training, customs, and so on. The rapid expansion of the regular army in the 1950s resulted in the introduction of multi-battalion regiments, the establishment of regimental depots and museums, and so forth. The three services were formally unified in 1968, and the adoption of a base system, the replacement of unit by individual rotation (to Germany), the closing of the depots, and similar measures all initially hit regiments hard. However, some of the ground then apparently lost has been regained in recent years. The regular regiments reacted to the seemingly threatening environment of the late 1960s by developing formidable institutional structures. At the same time, some of the symbols which disappeared after unification have been restored, and some of the autonomy surrendered to base staffs has been recovered.

There are similarities between the regiments of armies which promote the regimental system and those of armies which do not, most of them relating to operational aspects of military organisation. Where the regimental system differs from other forms of military organisation – such as the Israeli and German armies, with their civilian ethos, or the pre-1980 United States Army, with its centralised, and at the same time individualistic, character – is in its non-tactical structure, in the emphasis placed on symbolism and tradition, in the unit orientation of personnel policies and administrative practices, and in its highly-developed institutional format.

Regimental institutions – honorary appointments, regimental headquarters, veterans' associations, ladies'

system in the hope of improving motivation and cohesion.

The Regimental System

'Regiments' first appeared in England in about 1572, but they did not take their modern form until after the Cardwell-Childers reforms (1870-81), which linked regular battalions in pairs and gave the resulting regiments fixed bases (depots), from which much of their institutional structure, and their strongly territorial character, later developed. By 1914 the army was strongly characterised by its regimental spirit, and

auxiliaries, and so on – promote 'regimental affairs' (non-operational matters), with the goal of fostering distinctiveness, evoking unit pride, creating a community ambience, and in general establishing the ethos peculiar to each regiment. The symbolical aspects of the system – dress distinctions (especially the cap badge, 'that great talisman'[3]), colours, customs, ceremonial, and so on – foster the mystique, the uniqueness, and the 'in-group' orientation of each regiment, conferring that sense of belonging and of self-esteem (and also of ritual) which all successful groups, from motorcycle gangs to service clubs, give to their members.

Above all, the ethos of the regimental system is a corporate one, leading Brigadier Bidwell to describe the regiment as a social institution with a military function.[4]

Although the regimental system commands strong adherence, it has its critics, who point to the administrative problems it can create, its potential for rivalry and lack of cooperation, its conservatism, and its potential hindrance of organisational reform. Furthermore, commitment to the regiment varies among its members, probably more than many advocates of the system recognise. For example, Baynes may have exaggerated the generality of such commitment in pre-1914 regiments, and a 1979 survey of Canadian soldiers indicated that while junior combat troops supported the retention of regimental tradition, their support was considerably weaker that that of officers and senior NCOs;[5] furthermore, the responses to other survey items suggested that the rank-and-file were not particularly supportive of the vocational ethos.

Combat Motivation

Soldiers derive not only comradeship, but also a sense of security and protection, and a measure of self-esteem, from membership in the primary group (a social grouping frequently coterminous with the section), and cohesive groups reduce the potential for psychiatric breakdown and desertion among well-integrated members. While primary group cohesion normally contributes to combat effectiveness, there are plenty of examples where such groups have acted in opposition to

A cold weather evening the Officer's Mess, 1st Battalion, The Queen's Own Cameron Highlanders in India, 1932. (Painting by Col Monroe in *Officer's Mess: Life and Customs in the Regiments* by Lt Col R.J. Dickinson/Midas Books).

army requirements. Hence something is needed to link the primary group with the army as a whole. Such a link is more likely to flourish where primary group cohesion is complemented by pride of membership in the unit.

One of the most striking features of battle is the tendency towards paralysis and confusion which occurs when a unit first comes under fire, and it is particularly difficult to get soldiers moving once they have found shelter. In these circumstances leadership of any sort can exert a tremendous influence, given the tendency for people to copy the behaviour of others in threatening situations. Thus, one man rushing forward can stimulate others to advance, just as a man going rearward without explanation can start a panic. In a threatening environment, confidence – in the soldier's military skills, equipment, leaders and fellows – contributes to motivation and helps to offset fear.

The Regimental System and Combat Motivation

The regimental system influences the soldier's behaviour in battle in a number of ways. By promoting unit pride it builds the soldier's self-respect and confidence. It provides a focus of loyalty and a source of legitimation for those soldiers for whom abstract ideals have little attraction. By its relative stability it reinforces primary group cohesion. And, less directly perhaps, it influences the behaviour of the many by inspiring the behaviour of (often) the few.

Regimental pride has long been regarded as a valuable source of motivation. 'Everything that one can make of the soldiers consists in giving them an ésprit de corps, or, in other words, teaching them to place their regiment higher than all of the troops in the world,' Frederick the Great wrote.[6] On the other hand, such a feeling engenders confidence that the unit has the capability to master combat situations, and on the other it encourages every regiment to regard itself as an elite.

Men behave as they are expected to behave. In regiments in which historical achievement is strongly emphasised, part of that expectation is influenced by concern for corporate reputation. Just before a Second World War battle an infantry commanding officer recited the historical achievements of his regiment and then told his men: 'We've got to win our battles, whatever the cost, so that people will say "They were worthy descendants of the 32nd" and that's saying a hell of a lot.'[7] The historian of the Princess Patricia's Canadian Light Infantry served with the regiment in Korea, and later wrote: 'There was not a man in the PPCLI who did not firmly believe that the Patricias were the best soldiers in the Canadian Brigade ... He knew, too, that any action fought by the Regiment was watched and discussed by every other unit of the Brigade as well as by the British, Australians, New Zealanders and Indians of the Division. It mattered greatly to him what they thought of the Patricias.'[8]

This concern for reputation seems to be particularly strongly felt by regular soldiers, for whom it is axiomatic

Royal Canadian Regiment Pioneers on parade at Parliament Hill, Ottawa, in 1974.

that 'The professional soldier always fights.'[9] Baynes concluded unequivocally that regimental pride was the most important factor in the high morale of the 2nd Scottish Rifles at Neuve Chapelle (1915). Lord Moran and Robert Graves, neither of whom was a professional soldier, though both served with regular battalions, were equally convinced of the importance of regimental pride in the First World War. In his study of reciprocal non-aggression in the trenches, Ashworth found that some units rejected the live and let live system and were consistently aggressive; the four examples he cited were all regular battalions.[10] Likewise, in his study of combat soldiers of the Second World War, Ellis contended that regimental pride was not a major motivating factor (because of the influx of replacements), but an exception to which he referred was a regular battalion.[11] The

commanding officer of a regular battalion in that war was convinced that 'by far and away the greatest single factor in a soldier's morale is regimental pride . . .'.[12]

Perhaps some distinction should be made between *esprit* and regimental pride. Most successful and cohesive groups, military and non-military alike, share the former. While regimental pride is similarly characterised by pride of membership and unity of purpose, in multi-battalion regiments it assumes indentification with an entity more remote than the soldier's own unit. Sometimes such identification occurs, sometimes it may be muted. In a recent book on the British Army in the Second World War, General Sir David Fraser argued that for long-service regulars the regiment was the focus of *esprit* and loyalty, but 'For the majority . . . the focus of a man's loyalty was his own battalion, and he could feel isolated and bereft if moved from it, even to another battalion of the same regiment.[13]

Most soldiers need to have some justification, however inchoate, to legitimate doing something which few would do willingly. Patriotism, ideology, and belief in the country's war aims encourage many soldiers in the performance of their duties, or at least discourage doubt. But many people are more comfortable with smaller and less disputatious abstractions. Graves, for instance, thought that professional soldiers tended to be indifferent to issues.[14] A First World War staff officer claimed that 'The only incentive to the regular soldier was his regimental tradition.'[15] John Masters, who joined the British Army between the wars, claimed that 'men were shielded from disturbing doubts by the interposition of a smaller cause, which no one could cavil at, between themselves and the great national cause. Their spirit was and is built on the regiment.'[16] Equally, by their size and integration into the command and control network, it is much harder for major units to diverge from organisational goals than it is for section-sized units. Thus, cohesive units help to articulate primary groups into the larger organisation and to legitimate the missions assigned them.

Doubtless with the mass armies of the two world wars in mind, Montgomery asserted that regimental spirit was not a basic factor of morale because in the crisis of battle the majority of men will not derive encouragement from the glories of the past, but will seek aid from their leaders and comrades of the present.[17] In the context of units raised in wartime, particularly, the crucial word used by Montgomery was 'majority'. The literature of war clearly indicates that the behaviour of an individual, or of a small number of men, can exert an influence disproportionate to their numbers. 'The honour of my battalion and its opinion of me. Those are now my sustaining motives . . .', a British officer wrote in the First World War.[18] For some of the British soldiers surveyed by Holmes, a desire not to let down the regiment was an important motive.[19] Regimental pride may not always be the immediate catalyst in leadership acts by such men, but it will frequently be an important underlying motive, and if it helps to propel them forward, then it does exert an important, if indirect, influence on the followers, whatever the level of their commitment to the regiment. For example, a First World War attack by a new army battalion was on the verge of collapse when a private ran forward, roaring 'Heads up the Warwicks! Show the blighters your cap badges!' The men nearest him plunged forward again, followed by the rest of the line, and the enemy trench was taken.[20] Similarly, during a 1941 battle in North Africa, the adjutant of a regular battalion, though wounded, crawled up to a group of men: ' "Isn't this the Black Watch?" he cried. "Then – charge!" He waved us on with his stick and was instantly killed. We rose and took 'Tiger' with the bayonet . . .'.[21]

In battle, buddies and the group are of more immediate significance to most soldiers than is the unit. Nonetheless, the unit can play a significant role in primary group cohesion. It is well-recognised in military sociology that cohesion depends to a considerable extent on social stability. The regimental system actively promotes stability. Once a soldier is given a cap badge, he expects to retain it, even after absences for medical, training, or other reasons. Violation of this expectation can provoke resentment, as a mutiny among British troops at Salerno in 1943 indicated. Thus, the regimental system to some extent shelters the primary group from personnel practices which undermine stability, and hence cohesion. But in a long-drawn-out war, involving large numbers of men, it becomes progressively harder to fill a battalion's depleted ranks with soldiers only of the same regiment (in Italy in March 1944 it was formally agreed to regard infantry reinforcements as available for any battalion needing them). In such circumstances regimental spirit would probably decline as war-weary battalions become increasingly comprised of heterogeneous collections of replacements, trained in central depots.

To the extent that regimental spirit is a product of time – and Baynes claimed that even in 1914 it took two or three years before a regiment could claim a soldier as its own[22] – regular soldiers are probably more amenable to regimental socialisation than men enrolled in wartime. But while short-service soldiers seem to be influenced largely by social and situational factors, many have shown high levels of regimental commitment, largely because of the territorial nature of the system. A journalist who enrolled in the Second World War wrote how splendid it was to be part of a good regiment, 'and to feel that you must behave up to certain standards because of the regiment and its history . . .'[23]

The processes by which regiments socialise their members can also have negative implications for combat effectiveness. Group bonds are reinforced if aggression is directed at outsiders, but the rivalry induced thereby can sometimes impair mutual understanding and cooperation. The amalgamation of three depleted British regular battalions during the Second World War had unfortunate results: 'Loyalty to their regiment was imprinted very deep and perhaps carried with it feelings of antagonism for other regiments. In the early days of the . . . [new unit] the discord between the three elements was carried to extreme limits', one officer commented.[24] Bidwell contended that

'If morale is the prerequisite for waging war, the regimental system is justified; but like everything else in the world it has a price and the price of the regimental system is inefficiency and fragmentation, and also division in a field where co-operation is the next most important thing after morale.'[25]

**Commanding Officer, 2nd Regiment, Royal Canadian Horse
Artillery, seeks admission to City Hall, Kingston (Ontario),
when Freedom of City was conferred on Regiment.**

Nor is the regimental system the *sine qua non* of high *esprit* and motivation. The Canadian Expeditionary Force performed outstandingly in the First World War and had a notably high *esprit*. Yet the existing militia regimental structure was abandoned in 1914 and an *ad hoc* mobilisation plan implemented, whereby completely new units were raised (a few were based on existing regiments). In 1939 the existing regimental structure was used, and Canadian historians contend that it provided much of the army's strength and cohesion,[26] but Canadian units in North-West Europe cannot have surpassed the confidence, aggression, and *esprit* of the CEF.[27]

High motivation and *esprit* has been displayed by units in armies which do not use the regimental system. American soldiers often identify with higher formations, perhaps because they are more stable than regiments. By contrast, Israeli identification largely centres on the company (but also to some degree the brigade). The regimental system is foreign to the Israeli Army, and yet morale has been described as its secret weapon, so strong is it. The cohesion and high *esprit* of German units was very evident during the Second World War. Yet they were often cobbled together from men who were strangers to each other and to their officers, but who shared a sense of being Germans, soldiers, and comrades, and thus were able to cohere in even the most difficult circumstances.

Summary

Perhaps the strongest argument advanced in favour of the regimental system is the claim that it promotes cohesion and motivation in battle, and it clearly does enhance them, both directly and indirectly. In combat, primary group cohesion sometimes works against execution of the military mission. Parochial as the regimental system is, it limits dissension because it engages the loyalty of the crucial minority who provide leadership, and in the process legitimates organisational goals. Furthermore, in promoting the sense of belonging at the unit level, the regimental system uses personnel practices which have the effect of enhancing stability, and thereby cohesion, at the primary group level. But a war characterised by long duration, mass armies, and high casualties erodes the system's capability to promote stability. Nonetheless, for a key minority of soldiers the sense of belonging and the thrall of reputation seems to be remarkably enduring. A Canadian platoon commander in North-West Europe observed how fluid his battalion was, with the arrival of large numbers of replacements, 'the only fixed things being the hat badge and the strangely persistent *esprit*'.[28]

References

1. Richardson, MajGen F.M., *Fighting Spirit. A Study of Psychological Factors in War*, London: Leo Cooper, 1978, p. 16.
2. Baynes, John, *Morale. A Study of Men and Courage*, New York: Frederick A. Praeger, 1967, p. 163.
3. Bidwell, Shelford, *Modern Warfare: A Study of Men, Weapons and Theories*, London: Allen Lane, 1973, p. 139.
4. Bidwell, Brig R.G.S., 'The British Infantry Regiment', letter in *British Army Review*, No. 71, August 1982, p. 85.
5. Cotton, Maj C.A., *Military Attitudes and Values of the Army in Canada*, Willowdale: Canadian Forces Personnel Applied Research Unit, Report 79-5, December 1979, p. 58.
6. Luvaas, Jay, ed., *Frederick the Great on the Art of War*, New York: The Free Press, 1966, p. 78.
7. Quoted in Richardson, p. 22.
8. Williams, Jeffrey, *Princess Patricia's Canadian Light Infantry*, London: Leo Cooper Ltd, 1972, p. 78.
9. Janowitz, Morris, *The Professional Soldier. A Social and Political Portrait*, New York: The Free Press, 1964, p. 215.
10. Ashworth, Tony, *Trench Warfare, 1914-1918: The Live and Let Live System*, New York: Holmes & Meier, 1980, p. 21.
11. Ellis, John, *The Sharp End. The Fighting Man in World War II*, New York: Charles Scribner's Sons, 1980, p. 341.
12. Quoted in Holmes, Richard, *Firing Line*, London: Jonathan Cape, 1985, p. 314.
13. Fraser, David, *And We Shall Shock Them. The British Army in the Second World War*, London: Hodder and Stoughton, 1983, pp. 91-92.
14. Graves, Robert, *Goodbye to All That*, Harmondsworth: Penguin Books, 1973, p. 116.
15. Nicholson, Col W.N., *Behind the Lines*, London: Jonathan Cape, 1939, p. 147.
16. Masters, John, *Bugles and a Tiger. A Volume of Autobiography*, New York: The Viking Press, 1956, p. 121.
17. Montgomery, Field Marshal Viscount, *Morale in Battle: Analysis*, Germany: British Army of the Rhine, 1946, p. 21.
18. Quoted in Ellis, John, *Eye-Deep in Hell*, London: Croom Helm Ltd, 1976, p. 98.
19. Holmes, p. 278.
20. Slim, Field Marshal Sir William, *Courage, and Other Broadcasts*, London: Cassell & Company Ltd, 1959, pp. 85-86.
21. Quoted in Pitt, Barrie, *The Crucible of War. Western Desert 1941*, London: Futura Publications, 1980, p. 377.
22. Baynes, p. 163.
23. Millar, George, *Horned Pigeon*, London: Pan Books Ltd, p. 9.
24. Quoted in Ellis, *The Sharp End*, p. 341.
25. Bidwell, Shelford, *Gunners at War. A Tactical Study of the Royal Artillery in the Twentieth Century*, London: Arrow Books Ltd, 1972, p. 51.
26. See Granatstein, J.L., and Desmond Morton, *Bloody Victory. Canadians and the D-Day Campaign 1944*, Toronto: Lester & Orpen Dennys Limited, 1984, p. 235. See also Mowat, Farley, *The Regiment*, Toronto: McClelland and Stewart, 1955.
27. See Greenhous, Brereton, 'Canadians on D-Day – "Forty Years On, Growing Bolder and Bolder . . . " ', in *Canadian Defence Quarterly*, Vol. 14, No. 1, Summer 1984, pp. 36-40.
28. Pearce, Donald, *Journal of a War: North-West Europe 1944-1945*, Toronto; Macmillan of Canada, 1965, p. 157.

Exercise is Good For You

Military preparedness is not simply a matter of equipment; it is also a matter of troops who are well-trained in using that equipment, familiar with the tactics, familiar with the ground over which they may operate. To reach this state of preparedness constant training is necessary. We present a selection of pictures of military training and exercises which have come our way during the past year.

Overleaf
Top left: **Royal Marines bring their transport ashore in a Norwegian fiord.**

Bottom left: **Royal Netherlands Marines practising a river crossing.**

Right: **The cloak of invisibility: Polish radar technicians attempt to blend their radar set into the surroundings.**

◀ **'I thought *you* were bringing the rations!' US Special Forces during training in Panama.**

Above: **In mountain operations the mule still has a vital role. Troops of the 1st German Mountain Division loading a mule with part of a mountain howitzer.** (*P. Freytag*)

Right: **German 1st Mountain Division scaling an ice-wall in the Mont Blanc area.** (*P. Freytag*)

left: Crossing a river the hard way: an NCO of 101st US ...sion, demonstrating skills learned at the Jungle ...erations Training Centre in Panama.

...: A group of Gurkha soldiers awaiting orders during a ...ning exercise on Salisbury Plain.

...ove: Steak, chips and issue red wine: lunch-time for a ...rtuguese artillery battery during a NATO exercise.

...and over: Polish infantry practising a counter-attack ...noeuvre.

Polish troops take up a defensive position during annual exercises.

Top left: **Royal Netherlands Marines ski patrol in north Norway.**

Left: **No customers yet. Canadian medical corpsmen set up a field ambulance point in Norway.**

Above: **Members of the US 7th Infantry Battalion seen during Exercise Team Spirit '84, held in South Korea.**

The US Army's New Light Infantry Divisions

The Quest for Strategic Mobility and Combat Power

David C. Isby

M60 light machine gunner of the 82nd Airborne Division. The new 'lightened' 82nd will be joined by at least one light infantry division as part of XVIII Airborne Corps. (*US Army*)

Starting in 1985, the US Army began to deploy a new type of combat formation, the light infantry division. Optimised for low and medium intensity combat, these divisions are intended to be rapidly airlifted to potential conflicts as distant as the Persian Gulf or as near as Central America. By 1990, the Army will have five such divisions. Three of these will be new divisions – two active, one National Guard – although all will include existing units. Two will be formed by reorganising existing active infantry divisions.

American infantry now represents a broad range of capabilities. In addition to the mechanised infantry battalions equipped with M2 infantry fighting vehicles and M113 armoured personnel carriers, found in armoured and mechanised infantry divisions, there exists an airborne division, an air assault division, a motorised infantry division, a number of 'heavy' non-mechanised infantry divisions, and infantry remains the heart of the US Marine Corps four divisions.

The Army has pushed hard to get their new light infantry divisions, but questions remain as to their effectiveness. With the realisation that low and medium intensity conflict is indeed the most likely in the modern world, these divisions are optimised for that environment. Yet, if American infantry is to emerge victorious the next time it must go into combat, its capability on the battlefield and its capability to arrive on the battle field must both meet the challenges of a world that is more dangerous with each passing year.

Strategic Mobility and Combat Power

The idea of light infantry requires a compromise between combat power, sustainability, and strategic

The Alaska-based 6th Infantry Division (Light) will have a defensive mission. It will not be expected to deploy to cold-weather areas overseas. (*US Army*)

mobility. If a formation has the weapons needed for heavy fighting, or the combat and service support needed to keep it fighting for sustained periods, it is obviously going to require a lot of ships or aircraft to move.

The desire to have light units, self-contained but with a good 'teeth to tail' ratio, dates back to 1940, when, under the guidance of General Leslie McNair, chief of Army Ground Forces, the US Army's infantry divisions became smaller and lighter. In the 1960s, the need for light units manifested itself in the organisation of a number of independent light infantry and airborne brigades configured for counter-insurgency operations.

The strengths and the drawbacks of both the 1940 infantry division and the 1960s light infantry brigades may point out where the light infantry divisions of the late 1980s may encounter problems. Their organisation reflected the need to move the maximum number of

combat formations with the limited amount of strategic mobility forces – fast troop ships or transport aircraft, depending on the period – that were likely to be available. As the United States Army must be capable of fighting in theatres of operations that can be thousands of miles away from home, it must emphasize strategic mobility to a greater degree than any other Army.

All the US Army's light formations sought to do this by limiting equipment. None of these three types of light formations had any organic tanks or APCs. While the two types of divisions were to rely on the 105 mm howitzer as their primary artillery, the light infantry brigades were to have nothing heavier than 4.2-inch mortars.

The obvious problem – that the same 'lightness' desired for strategic mobility made the units less suitable for sustained combat, had the same obvious solution – the formation could be reinforced by corps-level independent units when required. This seemed an effective solution and also made efficient use of corps-level resources, which could then be concentrated under command of the divisions which need them the most.

Combat experience by both the 1940-organisation

Light infantry battalions will have four 81 mm mortars, with the standard US M29A1E1 to be replaced by the newer Anglo-Canadian model, which would have the capability of firing the Merlin guided munition. (*US Army*)

The man-carried Stinger is the only SAM currently intended to be in the light infantry division. (*US Army*)

infantry division in the Second World War and the light infantry brigades in Vietnam showed many lessons that may influence the future combat performance of the light infantry division. First, divisions work better with organic rather than attached elements. The infantry-tank and infantry-artillery teamwork so vital to success on the modern battlefield cannot be improvised. Infantrymen have learned, with good reason, to distrust tanks they have never seen before. Accounts of US Army actions in the Battle of the Bulge and the coordination problems between British Commonwealth armour and infantry in the Western Desert are evidence of this. This led to the second lesson: that light formations will tend to 'heavy up' when faced with sustained combat. US infantry divisions in the Second World War soon 'acquired' their own tank and tank destroyer battalions from corps, which became *de facto* divisional units. In Vietnam, the light infantry brigades acquired tube artillery. Some became part of a standard infantry division – the Americal – which had the

problems inherent in a division that had never trained together as a unit before being committed to the theatre of operations.

The Light Infantry Division and its Mission

At the end of the Vietnam War, the US Army put its emphasis on developing and modernising its heavy, mechanised forces. These forces had taken second place in both new hardware and operational and tactical thinking since counter-insurgency operations gained priority in the early 1960s. The new emphasis reflected not only the primary threat the Army had to face – a Soviet invasion of Central Europe – but the realities of American politics. Low and medium intensity armed conflicts were simply not politically feasible.

The fall of Iran, the invasion of Afghanistan and the spread of Communist insurgency in Central America, along with passing of the more visible and tractable symptoms of America's political 'post-Vietnam malaise' made it evident that the United States had more of a need to project power than it had capability. The

The standard US Army medium anti-tank weapon, the M47 Dragon, has not proven a complete success in service. Its range of 1 km makes it basically a self-defence weapon. (*US Army*)

formation of the Rapid Deployment Joint Task Force, which became Central Command, brought home the difficulty in fighting on the other side of the world, without the established logistical base that the US forces have in Europe. By the early 1980s, to meet its Central Command commitments to insert forces into the Persian Gulf area and elsewhere, the US Army started to examine the possibility of deploying a division more easily deployable than either the 82nd Airborne or 101st Airborne (Air Assault), the two divisions that the Army would be first to commit to a Central Command contingency.

The idea of light divisions were supported by the then Army Chief of Staff, General Edward C. Meyer. He assigned his Vice Chief of Staff, General John A. Wickham, to be the high-level proponent of this concept. When General Wickham became Chief of Staff, he continued his support of the light infantry division concept. The new divisions, as envisioned, would have to have a better teeth-to-tail ratio than other US divisions, minimising service support functions, which led to a requirement for an austere support base for the light division. Primary combat environment was seen as the passes of the Zagros Mountains of central Iran. It would have the capability for blunting an armoured offensive, while being able to strike northwards with heliborne units. In addition, such divisions would have to protect the area between the Zagros and the Allied airheads from Soviet airborne and heliborne attacks.

In addition, if it ever becomes necessary to commit US combat troops into Latin America, a light infantry force would be more effective than a mechanised combined arms force.

A tripod-mounted TOW ATGM. Each of the light infantry division's nine infantry battalions will have four TOWs. Unlike the 82nd Airborne or Bundeswehr light brigades, there will be no brigade-level anti-tank company. (*US Army*)

TOW missile launcher mounted on an M-151 Jeep.

Strategic Mobility and the Light Infantry Division

A light infantry division can be lifted to the Persian Gulf in about 500 sorties by C-141 Starlifter transport aircraft. This could be accomplished, the Army estimates, in four days. In comparison, a standard infantry division would require 1,433 C-141 sorties, moving 31,260 tons of cargo, rather than 12,837 tons for the light infantry division, and would require 12.4 days for the division to reach the Persian Gulf. The light infantry division does not require the use of C-5A aircraft to move, while a standard infantry division needs the big airlifters for its armoured battalion and heavy engineer equipment.

The 105 mm M102 howitzer – used in Vietnam and Grenada – will be the mainstay of the light infantry division's artillery. (*US Army*)

This is possible because the configuration that was approved for the light infantry division is intended to create a force that has strategic mobility (by being easier to airlift than existing divisions) at the expense of, first, tactical mobility (the number of trucks and helicopters would have to be limited), second, firepower (lots of heavy weapons would increase the airlift requirement – no tracked vehicles other than a few M9 armoured bulldozers would be included) and, third, sustainability (the light scale of service support means that the division will need help to operate its own).

It has been suggested that in organising the light infantry divisions, the Army is duplicating the functions of the Marine Corps. The Army units, however, are more oriented to air deployment and they are not tied to off-shore support and amphibious shipping as is the Marine Corps. The Army believes that the augmentation possible through its force structure gives the light infantry division greater flexibility than a comparable Marine unit.

Light Divisions Join the Army: 1985-1990

The 7th Infantry and 25th Infantry Divisions at Ford Ord, California and Schofield Barracks, Hawaii, respectively, will be converted from standard infantry divisions. Conversion of the 7th started in September,

---

Personnel total: 10,768. Equipment totals: M16 rifle (in infantry battalions), 3,465; M203, 522; SAW, 670; 7.62 mm LMG, 162; TOW (ground mouting), 36; 60 mm mortar, 54; 81 mm mortar, 36; motorcycles, 135; HMMWV light truck, 306; Dragon, 72; 155 mm howitzer, 8; 105 mm howitzer, 54; Vulcan, 18; Stinger, 40; AH-1, 29; OH-58, 31; UH-60, 36.
Notes: 1) Services include MP company and signals, maintenance, supply and transport, combat electronic warfare and intelligence and medical battalions. 2) There is a possibility that British 105 mm Light Guns may be purchased instead of 105 mm howitzers.

1984 and was finished on 1 October, 1985. The 25th will convert during fiscal year 1986. Because of the smaller size of light infantry divisions, both divisions will have three brigades of active Army infantry, rather than two active Army brigades and one National Guard round-out brigades, from Oregon for the 7th and Hawaii for the 25th. The army believes that having the 7th and 25th all-active divisions will increase readiness and make them more easily deployable. It will also make deploying them politically easier, as no reservists will have to be mobilised.

A third light infantry division, the 29th Infantry Division, is to be a National Guard formation, with its headquarters at Fort Belvoir, Virginia. Formed in late 1984, the 29th consists of two pre-existing component brigades from the Maryland and Virginia National Guard, with a third brigade organised in 1985.

Personnel total: 552. Equipment totals: M16 rifle, 385; M203, 58; SAW, 58; 7.62 mm LMG, 18; TOW, 4; 60 mm mortar, 6; 81 mm mortar, 4; motorcycles, 15; HMMWV, 34.

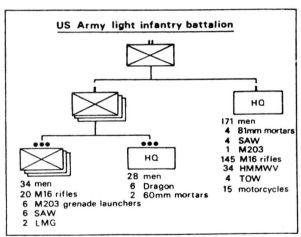

US Army light infantry battalion

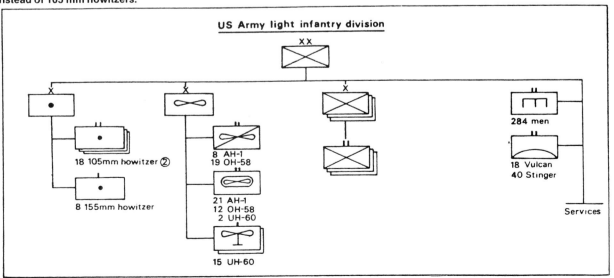

US Army light infantry division

The remaining two light infantry divisions are new units. The 10th Mountain Division was established in 1984 at Fort Drum, New York, although it lacks a nearby Military Airlift Command base. The 1st brigade – with four infantry battalions – will move to Fort Drum in 1986-87, as soon as barracks are built. A second brigade will be formed at Fort Benning, Georgia – with two infantry battalions – and will remain there until its barracks are built at Fort Drum in 1989. The 10th's third brigade will be a round-out National Guard unit – the 27th Brigade of the New York National Guard. While it carries on the title of the famous 10th Mountain Division of the Second World War, it is not proposed to give the division special mountain warfare training at this time.

The 6th Division was created in 1985 at Fort Richardson, Alaska, by re-designating the current 172nd Infantry Brigade. Its 2nd Brigade will be formed at Fort Wainwright, Alaska, in fiscal year 1987. The division's 3rd brigade will also be a 'round-out' unit, the 205th Infantry Brigade of the US Army Reserve, headquartered at Fort Snelling, Minnesota, a unit which has long specialised in cold-weather operations.

There have been Congressional proposals to form a sixth light infantry division from the two former round-out brigades of the 7th and 25th, largely motivated by concern that these units may have their currently high priorities on equipment and training reduced now that they are 'orphan' brigades. It is possible that the 42nd Division of the New York National Guard – now that its 27th Brigade has been removed – may also be converted to the new organisation.

The 82nd Airborne and 101st Airborne (Air Assault) divisions will also be reorganised to make them 'lighter' and more deployable, with strengths of 13,000 and 15,000 soldiers respectively. The reduction will not affect 'foxhole' strength, and will largely be accomplished by transferring some service support functions to non-divisional units.

Organisation for Combat

The light infantry division is basically a smaller version of existing US infantry divisions, with the armoured and mechanised infantry battalions absent. Its nine 543-man infantry battalions are organised into three brigades. Division artillery consists of three battalions with 18 105 mm M102 howitzers each, plus a battery of eight 155 mm M198 howitzers. The Combat Aviation Brigade has 29 AH-1 attack helicopters, 36 UH-60 Blackhawk transport helicopters and 31 OH-58A Scout helicopters. An air defense battalion with 18 improved towed Vulcan 20 mm guns and 40 Stinger man-portable SAM launchers, as well as a military intelligence/reconnaissance battalion, a light combat engineer battalion, an MP company and a signals battalion

provide combat support. An austere 1180-man Divisional Service Command (DISCOM) provides service support.

Configured for easy airlift and use in low and medium intensity conflicts, the Army plans to support light infantry divisions deployed to the theatre of operations with additional units if sustained combat is expected.

Designated the 'Round-Up' concept, this augmentation can include independent heavy brigades, artillery, air defense, engineers, or service support units. The Army hopes that this will allow light infantry divisions to be effective throughout the spectrum of conflict. How effective this would be in practice is uncertain. The light infantry divisions would certainly have to train with

Light infantry divisions will have one eight-gun battery of 155 mm M198 howitzers for general support missions. The 'standard' infantry divisions and the Marine divisions will continue to use the M198 as their standard divisional artillery piece. (*US Army*)

their proposed augmentation forces in peacetime if they are to cooperate effectively in war.

One way the Army is planning to reconcile the need for lightness for strategic mobility with the need for heaviness for sustained combat is by the organisation of at least one new 'Round-Up' brigade. They will not be part of the light divisions, but will rather be independent units. Such brigades could, however, be tasked to be put under the command of a specific light infantry division if it is committed to a situation that requires heavy force support.

One new 'Round-Up' brigade is planned to be formed from the one tank battalion with M60A3s and the one mechanised infantry battalion equipped with M113s that were previously organic to both the 7th and 9th Infantry Divisions under their previous organisations.

The Light Division in Battle

As do all US Army divisions, the light infantry division will fight according to the operational guidelines of the 1982 edition of FM 100-5, *Operations*, the US Army's 'capstone' manual of operational-level combat. The light infantry division will fight in close cooperation with both Army and Air Force aircraft. Because of the light infantry division's lack of organic long-range firepower, it will have a high need for close air support sorties, which will mean that it will have to be adept at the 'Airland Battle' that FM 100-5 espouses.

FM 100-5's concept of operations require high tactical mobility by US units to counterattack, redeploy, and engage rapidly developing threats. The light infantry division will need support from non-organic elements to do this effectively, for the division can only lift one battalion each by truck or helicopter. Everyone else walks. With organic transport limited, bringing supplies forward from the rear of the division boundary will absorb a considerable percentage of the division's transport strength.

The light infantry division, however, is orientated towards medium and low intensity conflicts, while FM 100-5 is aimed toward large-scale conventional conflict against an enemy with large, mechanised combined arms forces, numerical superiority and lots of tanks, artillery, and helicopters.

This does not mean that the light division will not have to face such a threat. There are very few primitive battlefields left in the world. The potential aggressors of today come heavily equipped with armour, surface-to-air missiles, helicopters, and other systems that 20 years ago were the province of industrialised nations. The North Korean Army has, in addition to a large unconventional warfare capability, many divisions equipped with tanks and APCs. Even Nicaragua has

Infantrymen of the 25th Division on exercises in Hawaii. The light division's divisional engineers will not have any bridging capability, making operations like this more likely. (*US Army*)

The UH-60 Blackhawk will be used as the standard lift helicopter in the division's Combat Aviation Brigade. If required, ground combat units can be placed under command of this brigade headquarters. (*US Army*)

over 300 armoured vehicles. Libya and Syria both have large numbers of Soviet-built tanks in their order of battle. Against such a force, light infantry, to survive must either hold difficult terrain (the Zagros Mountains could provide a series of passable imitations of Monte Cassino), dig itself in to substantial field fortifications, or be completely mobile in helicopters or all-terrain vehicles.

The Army believes that the light infantry division will have to deal with such a threat as part of a corps that includes heavier units or, if a corps has not been deployed, then the light infantry division will have to fight with additional reinforcing units under divisional command or need additional air support. While a light infantry division, with its tactical mobility increased by additional trucks and helicopters, either pre-positioned or taken over from NATO countries, could be effective in the rear area protection mission, it is likely that a light infantry division in Europe could find itself in the forward division area, especially in dense terrain such as the Hessian hills or the more mountainous parts of

Bavaria. The dense conurbations of Germany could also be defended by light infantry.

The US Army's '10-10' commitment to NATO – to have ten divisions on the line in Germany ten days after mobilisation – requires the deployment of a fifth and sixth set of POMCUS pre-positioned equipment. The Army has proposed making these two sets of equipment for the 7th and 25th Infantry Divisions. Light infantry divisions will certainly have a NATO mission. Unless the Army re-evaluates its commitments, however, then these divisions may have to have their structure modified for effective use in a European environment.

FM 100-5's battle concept includes an increased emphasis on night operations, both offensive and defensively. The light infantry division reflects this with its use of large amounts of night vision equipment and by the high priority on night operations in TRADOC's (The US Army Training and Doctrine Command) 'Fight Light' program.

Through 'Fight Light', TRADOC is trying to maximise the potential contributions light infantry divisions can make to the overall battle, while minimising its vulnerabilities. The Army is also trying to build up a 'light infantry' spirit, with Ranger-type training and a proposed 'Light Infantry' shoulder tab. But there is a lot more than motivation at stake. US infantry has, since the Second World War, relied heavily on 'outside' firepower – from artillery and airpower – in combat. The light infantry divis- ion will have to rely on its own fire- power. If it is to prove effective, 'fighting light' will have to include not only fighting differently, but think- ing differently as well.

Hardware

The US Army needs forces such as the light infantry divisions. It remains to be seen whether they are effectively equipped for their mission. The quality of individual weapons systems is even more important in a light infantry division than in a mechanised, combined-arms unit. Accuracy is important, because the division cannot prevail be sheer weight of metal alone. Maximum use of high-accuracy, high-effectiveness weapons systems will also make re-supply more feasible, especially considering the limited number of trucks or helicopters that are likely to be available.

Most US Army weapons are not designed for the type of missions that the light infantry division will be asked to undertake. In many cases, off-the-shelf purchases of the weapons systems used by allied light forces would increase the capabilities of the light infantry division.

The US Army is already evaluating 20 British-built 105 mm Light Guns, with a 17 km maximum range rather than the 105 mm M102 howitzers with an 11.6 km range currently projected as the only tube artillery piece in the light infantry division. Divisions organised

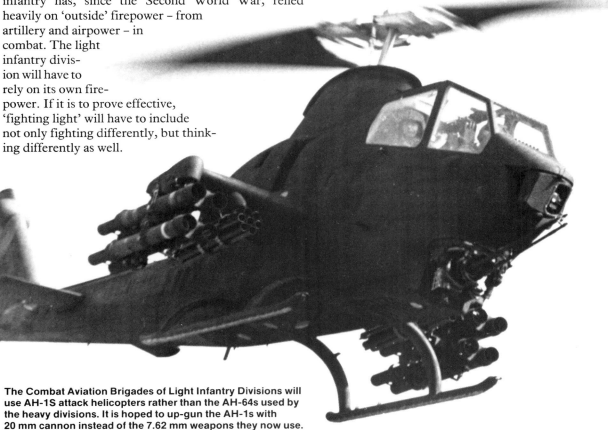

The Combat Aviation Brigades of Light Infantry Divisions will use AH-1S attack helicopters rather than the AH-64s used by the heavy divisions. It is hoped to up-gun the AH-1s with 20 mm cannon instead of the 7.62 mm weapons they now use. (US Army)

The M72A3 66 mm LAW's limitations as an anti-tank weapon are perhaps more critical in a light infantry division than elsewhere, because the infantryman has to depend on his own firepower. (*US Army*)

on the Soviet model use the 122 mm D-30 howitzer with a 15.3 km range so the light infantry division is in danger of being out-ranged by opposition that has adequate artillery. While it appears likely the Light Gun will be procured, the advanced ammunition that would allow them to outrange a 122 mm howitzer probably will not be used by the US Army.

The light infantry division has limited numbers of TOW anti-tank guided missile launchers – each infantry battalion has four, compared to 22 for a US mechanised infantry battalion. This not only limits the light division's ability to deal with Soviet-style mechanised forces in any except rough terrain, but also makes the man-portable ATGMs more important. However, the light infantry division will use the same Dragon ATGM as the rest of the Army. The anti-tank capability of the light infantry division would be greatly increased without a corresponding increase in the infantry's load if the Dragons were replaced by the Euromissile MILAN

ATGM used by most NATO armies. With twice the range of the Dragon and with the MIRA thermal imaging night sight, light units can rely on MILANs more than Dragons as an effective anti-tank defense. The MILAN/MIRA combination was being evaluated by the US Army for possible use as an Army-wide Dragon replacement in mid-1985.

The problem of anti-tank defense, however, is going to be a limit of the usefulness of the light infantry divisions in a Central European scenario. They simply do not have enough tank-killing systems even for operations in urban or close terrain.

The ability of light infantry divisions to defend against armoured forces remains one of the key questions of their future viability. Light infantry without adequate anti-tank weapons cannot defeat determined combined-arms mechanised attacks. Arnhem showed that. On the other hand, light infantry forces with adequate anti-tank weapons and tactics can effectively defend against tanks, as was shown when Egyptian infantry held against Israeli attacks in the closing days of the 1973 war. With the main battle tank now no longer limited to industrialised nations – Libya has more tanks in inventory than Great Britain – the light infantry division's anti-tank capability is likely to be put to the test in even a medium intensity conflict.

Will the light infantry division's anti-tank capability prove effective against armoured opponents in Europe and elsewhere? The number of weapons is not large, especially when compared to other infantry units intended to operate on NATO's central front as mobile anti-tank blocking forces, such as the British 6th Airmobile Brigade, the German *Fallschirmjäger* brigades, and the infantry regiment of the French 4th *Division Aeromobile*. These have infantry battalions with over 40 long-range (2 km+) tank-killing systems, while the infantry battalions of the light infantry division have only four TOWs.

One of the limitations of the current light infantry division organisation is the lack of a central anti-tank reserve. There is no one unit the divisional commander can quickly shift to meet an enemy *Schwerpunkt* (point of main attack) except his attack helicopters and possibly a company of heliborne infantry. Yet, the attack helicopters are likely to have their hands full with enemy

helicopters and air defenses, both likely to be generously allocated to support a *Schwerpunkt*.

The air defense of the light infantry division is also limited, using only Stinger man-portable SAMs and towed 20 mm Vulcan anti-aircraft guns. A system such as the British Rapier SAM that was used effectively in the Falklands, or the French Crotale SAM is needed to supplement these systems, otherwise enemy fixed wing air or helicopters will encounter only local opposition.

If the US is going to try and field an effective light force, it should not expect it to fight with weapons not intended for that type of operation. The US Army has worked on its Light Armoured Vehicle (LAV) project on a stop-and-go basis, but if they ever decide to proceed with the project, the LAV could make a contribution to the light infantry division.

Tactical mobility is intentionally limited in the light

The 60 mm mortar will be used in the rifle companies of the light infantry battalions – two tubes per rifle company. (*US Army*)

How most of the light infantry division will move – on foot. The division has enough truck and helicopter lift to move one infantry battalion by each means, but resupply requirements will cut down on the availability of this lift capability. (*US Army*)

infantry division. If personnel are available, it is possible trucks can be requisitioned in the theatre of operations, but unless non-divisional assets are provided, the lack of tactical mobility may prove a drawback. The 6th Division's mobility will be enhanced by the order of Swedish-designed Bv 206 over-snow vehicles.

Concepts and Capabilities

The concept behind the light infantry division has much to recommend it. While the central front in Europe must remain the most important point of focus for the US Army, it is not the most likely location for a future conflict. There, the ability to deploy forces quickly is the key to force projection. It is better to have a battalion on the scene for a decisive battle than have a division arrive too late.

This underlines the importance of improving US strategic mobility forces. The combination of Air Force transport aircraft, Navy fast amphibious transport ships, and the use of Maritime pre-position equipment ships will continue to be the chief determinant of US ability to project forces into the Persian Gulf, rather than the configuration of the Army divisions to be sent there.

With the elimination of any real growth in defense spending in the US budget for the 1986 fiscal year, the Army's plans to deploy new light infantry divisions have come under intense financial pressure. None of the planned deployments have been cancelled, but they are likely to be delayed. The Army is looking into obtaining commercial mortgage financing for the expansion of the Fort Drum facilities.

How can the US Army improve the capability of its light infantry divisions without defeating the need for mobility and imposing additional financial and manpower requirements the Army cannot afford? Some approaches could yield considerable return on the marginal investment dollar.

1. *Procure The Best Available Off The Shelf Equipment for The Light Infantry Divisions.*

The Army policy that the light infantry divisions will be formed with 'off the shelf' equipment is probably a good one, but it need not be limited to the US shelf. This applies especially to:

Milan ATGM with MIRA thermal sights (most important single item)
British 105 mm Light Guns (with long barrels and advanced ammunition)
Rapier or Crotale SAMs
Sniper rifles
A 'mini-RPV'

This will complicate US Army training and logistics, but will pay dividends on the battlefield. Financial costs could be reduced by negotiating sale-back agreements with the sellers or, if the US develops suitable replacements for these systems at mid-life, they could then be transferred to needy allies such as Turkey or Thailand.

2. *Assign a 'Round-Up' Guard or Reserve TLAT TOW Battalion to Each Light Division.*

These battalions are currently considered corps assets. Found only in the National Guard, they consist of 60 jeep-mounted TOWs. By retraining five Guard or Reserve infantry or support battalions and giving them enough TOWs (30-40 systems) to be smaller versions of these battalions, the light division would have the anti-tank reserve that it currently lacks.

3. *Trucks to Motorise Light Infantry Divisions Should be Available in Europe.*

This could be accomplished by pre-positioning US Army trucks or earmarking German civilian trucks for use on arrival.

4. *Intelligence Assets Should be Optimised for Low and Medium Intensity Conflict.*

'Round-Up' assets could be provided for specific contingencies.

5. *Light Infantry Divisions Should Keep Units on Alert for Short-Notice Deployment, Similar to the Way the 82nd Airborne Does.*

These divisions should have a 'point' company and battalion ready to move in hours. Pre-packaged equipment should be divided into C-141 loads and kept at the nearest airbase. The Army currently has plans to do this with the 7th Infantry Division. Other divisions may follow suit. Current plans are that at least one light infantry division will be subordinated to the XVIII (Airborne) Corps, while it is likely at least one other will become part of I Corps, tasked for both Persian Gulf and Pacific contingencies.

However, the readiness base on which the light divisions are to be established is somewhat shaky. The 172nd Brigade and the 7th and 25th Divisions all had substantial deficiencies before shifting to light infantry organisation.

A force optimised for high strategic mobility should be ready to move. But while, overall, dollars spent on strategic mobility assests, carrier battle groups, or Marine amphibious forces may have more immediate and direct return in terms of US capabilities for power projection to distant contingencies, the light infantry divisions will certainly add to the overall perception of our willingness to project such forces.

This perception is needed if we are to extend our concept of deterrence into areas where there have not been traditional commitments of US forces. The Soviet Union knows that if it attacks Western Europe, and North Korea knows that if it attacks South Korea, they will find US forces fighting against them. The problem is how to create this same deterrent effect for, say, an Iranian attack on Kuwait or a Nicaraguan invasion of Costa Rica. Neither contingencies is likely, but neither or the two potential victims has the benefit of a long-standing deployment of US forces, to show that we will, in fact, fight against an aggressor.

In 1982, Argentina invaded the Falkland Islands because they thought the British had neither the capability nor the will to eject them. They had been led to believe this by the fact that the British had just not cared much about the Falklands and that they were busily engaged in dismantling much of their power projection capability. The British had undercut their own conventional deterrence.

The liberation of the Falklands was a great success for the British armed services. It would have been an even better success had they persuaded the Argentinians not to try their luck in the first place. The light infantry divisions, in addition to the 82nd, 101st, and the Marines will have their main mission in trying to deter future aggressors from thinking the US has not the will or the means to protect friendly nations.

Cannon All Round Them

Charles Castle

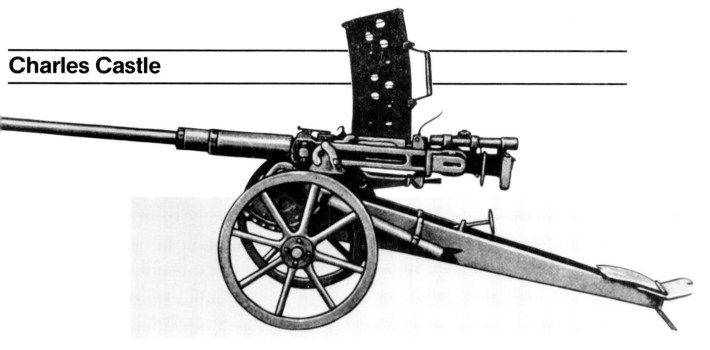

The Semag-Becker cannon on its light wheeled carriage, offered as an infantry support and anti-tank gun in the middle 1920s. (*Photo courtesy Oerlikon-Buhrle*)

'Cannon' means different things to different people. When the poet wrote of 'Cannon to right of them, cannon to left of them ...' he was referring to smoothbore muzzle-loading artillery; when the staff officer talks about 'cannon artillery' he is differentiating between conventional artillery and missile-armed artillery regiments. But to the soldier of the 1980s 'cannon' has come to mean just one thing – light, automatic, small-calibre guns which are, in some respects, overgrown machine guns. For many years cannon have been principally an aircraft weapon; their only application to ground troops was in the light anti-aircraft role. But today more and more cannon are appearing on the land battlefield and there are moves afoot to make them a replacement for heavy machine guns in some applications. In view of this sudden interest, perhaps a closer look at the cannon is justified.

The origin of today's cannon can be quite precisely located: Willich, Germany, in 1913. There, two brothers named Conders, employees of the Stahlwerke Becker, set about designing a heavier type of machine gun which would fire an explosive shell and be a suitable weapon for arming aircraft. Hitherto, because of the St

Petersburg Convention of 1868, explosive projectiles weighing less than 400 g were outlawed as anti-personnel weapons. In practice this placed a lower calibre limit of 37 mm on gun designers, and just how the Conders brothers reconciled their adoption of a 19 mm shell weighing about 130 g with this restriction is far from clear. They probably argued that it was intended as an anti-material weapon rather than anti-personnel.

The gun they designed was a fairly simple blowback weapon, feeding from a 15-shot box magazine and with a rate of fire of 300 rounds per minute. In view of the considerable power of the cartridge, the gun used the 'differential locking' principle to secure the breech. The design was such that the heavy bolt was actually moving forward at the instant of firing, so that the recoil force first had to arrest the bolt, then reverse it and accelerate it rearward, and this reversal of movement served to hold the breech closed against the chamber pressure for enough time to allow the shell to leave the gun muzzle.

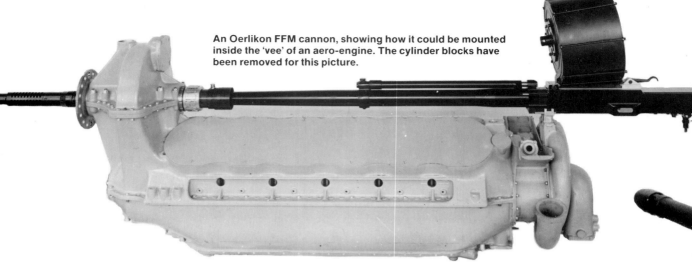

An Oerlikon FFM cannon, showing how it could be mounted inside the 'vee' of an aero-engine. The cylinder blocks have been removed for this picture.

(Much the same system is widely used on sub-machine guns today.)

Simple as it may have been, it was 1916 before the Becker cannon was perfected to the point where it could be submitted for military testing. In 1917 approval was given and production began, the intention being to use it to arm the Gotha bombers then raiding England. In addition a number were issued to the German Army as air defence weapons. Precisely how many were built is unknown, but after the Armistice in 1918 the Allied Disarmament Commission confiscated and destroyed 392 guns.

After the war the Stahlwerke Becker, like most other German firms, was forbidden to engage in weapons production and they therefore sold their patents and tooling to a Swiss company, the Seebach Maschinenbau AG (Semag). This firm made some small improvements, changed the calibre to 20 mm, and placed the result on the market as the Semag-Becker Cannon, a lightweight infantry support gun on a two-wheeled mount. They also touted it as the answer to the tank. But it failed to find any takers, and in 1924 Semag went bankrupt.

As one door closes, another opens; in 1924 George Buhrle, the manager of the Oerlikon Machine Tool Works of Switzerland was looking around for some other product for his factory to manufacture. He bought up the patents and tooling and hired some of the staff of the defunct Semag company, set up a production line and sent his salesmen out with a new line. Before the year was out the Oerlikon gun (as it was now known) had been sold to Finland and Mexico and the Oerlikon company was on its way to world-wide fame.

The Oerlikon cannon was adopted widely in the 1930s as an aircraft and light anti-aircraft gun and toyed with by several armies as potential anti-tank weapon, though few adopted it for that role. It also acted as a stimulant to other designers: in 1931, when the Dewoitine D.501 fighter was being designed for the French Air Force the Hispano-Suiza company, building the V-12 engine, wanted to mount a cannon inside the engine vee so as to

fire through the propeller boss. The French would not tolerate an imported weapon, so Hispano set to work to design their own 20 mm cannon, though they had to license some patented components from Oerlikon. The result was the HS9, which used a gas piston to unlock the breech, after which blowback drove the breechblock back and reloaded the gun.

In 1918 the German firm Rheinmetall of Düsseldorf had developed a 20 mm gun which was, in effect, an enlarged Dreyse machine gun. This had been designed by Louis Schmeisser in 1907 and was a recoil-operated weapon using a hinged breechblock which was cammed in and out of engagement by tracks in the gun body. The

cannon on the world market: the blowback Oerlikon, the delayed-blowback Hispano-Suiza, and the recoil-operated Solothurn. Virtually anything else of any consequence which had a different name turned out to be a copy of one of these, either with or without benefit of a license.

We need not investigate the progress of design during the Second World War too deeply, since much of it was simply gradual improvement or adaptation to newer types of aircraft, but there are two significant steps which must be mentioned. The first was the German conclusion that the 20 mm shell had had its day and that something heavier was needed to put a bomber aircraft out of action. The second, stemming from this, was the Mauser development of a 30 mm calibre 'revolver cannon', which introduced a new mechanical principle into the firearms world.

The revolver cannon used a fixed barrel with, behind it, a revolving five-chambered cylinder similar to that of an ordinary hand revolver pistol. A gas piston operated a

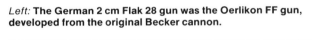

Left: **The German 2 cm Flak 28 gun was the Oerlikon FF gun, developed from the original Becker cannon.**

Right: **A French 30 mm revolver cannon, showing the cylindrical casing around the revolving unit.**

20 mm gun was almost completed when the war ended, and the drawings, tools and prototypes were smuggled out to Holland, to remain undisturbed until 1929. They were then shipped off to a Rheinmetall subsidiary in Switzerland, the Solothurn company, which thereafter developed the weapon and put it on the market. In 1934 the design was accepted by the German Navy and Luftwaffe as their standard light air defence gun.

In 1939, therefore, there were three basic 20 mm

reciprocating slide which governed the operation of various components; firstly it revolved the cylinder by means of a cam, secondly it extracted the fired cases, and thirdly it loaded the new rounds. Assuming the cylinder is empty, the action would proceed as follows: manual or mechanical cocking would retract the operating slide which would rotate a star wheel to draw the ammunition belt into the gun and present a round for feeding. A second retraction would pull the round from the belt and load it into an empty chamber, pulling the next round in at the same time. A third retraction would align the loaded chamber with the barrel, load the second chamber, and prepare the third round. As the chamber turned, so the base of the loaded round was forced in front of a standing breech containing an electrical stud; to fire, an electrical impulse was switched down this stud to fire the electric primer in the cartridge. The gas pressure of the fired round would then operate the piston and the slide, the cylinder would revolve one step, positioning round 2, loading round 3, preparing round 4, and extracting the empty case from round 1. And so the cycle would continue. One advantage of this mechanism was that it could be contained in a much shorter receiver, since there was no call for a long bolt movement to absorb recoil and cycle the action.

In the immediate postwar years the revolver cannon was examined closely by many designers and adopted in several countries. It formed the basis for the development of the Aden gun in Britain, the DEFA gun in France, the Oerlikon 206RK and the M39 in the United States. Their principal virtues, particularly for aircraft armament engineers, was their compact size and their high rate of fire, attributable to the fact that the ammunition was being fed into and extracted from the gun in stages. The American M39, for example, could fire at 1600 rounds per minute, and with the short duration of firing time in aerial dogfights, due to the increased speed of jet aircraft, it was important to get as high a number of shots into the target as possible.

Even 1600 rounds a minute was not sufficient for some designers, though, and the Americans resuscitated the Gatling Gun of the 19th century, built it in 20 mm calibre and drove it with an electric motor to obtain rates as high as 6000 shots per minute. The Gatling takes the revolver principle to its logical conclusion by using six barrels, rather than one barrel and five chambers. The drawback to the revolver gun was that the high rate of fire soon heated up and wore out the solitary barrel; by using six barrels, and loading them by stages, firing one at a time as it reached a specific point in the rotation, and unloading by stages, five barrels were free-wheeling and cooling down while one fired.

With this, the aerial fighters had what they wanted, a weapon which could put 100 shots into the target in one second, and the Gatling principle, as applied by the General Electric Company, has been widely adopted. Even the Soviets latched on to it and built it for their aircraft. But it does have the drawback that in large calibres – 30 mm for example – it becomes a sizeable piece of equipment, and only applicable to aircraft capable of carrying the weight and stowing the bulk.

The Gatling, with its external power source, also demonstrated another useful feature: it was not stopped by a faulty cartridge. Self-powered weapons, fed with a cartridge which refuses to fire, come to a sudden stop; the Gatling gun simply continues revolving and ejects the faulty round, merely missing a beat as it does so. There was always the theoretical danger that the misfire might turn out to be a hangfire and explode after it had been ejected, but at the speed the Gatling was revolving there was so much impetus behind the ejection that the offender was likely to be out of dangerous distance before it went off. And in any case, statistically the chances of a hangfire were negligible.

And so when the US Army approached the Hughes Helicopter Company in the early 1970s with a request for a new gun capable of firing the existing 20 mm M50 cartridge, Hughes looked at external power. They had already done some experimenting in 7.62 mm calibre and were soon able to demonstrate a totally new concept, the 'Chain Gun'. In this weapon the heart of the mechanism is an endless loop of chain passing around the floor of the receiver and coupled, by a lug, to a bolt carrier. Thus, supposing the bolt to be closed, the movement of the chain to the rear, along one side of the receiver, draws back the bolt carrier which, by a cam groove acting on a lug on the bolt, revolves the bolt to unlock it. Further rearward movement of the carrier now opens the bolt and ejects the empty cartridge case. By this time the carrier has reached the rear of the receiver and it rests there while the moving chain proceeds across the back of the gun and turns to go forward on the other side. This movement then carries the bolt carrier forward to load a fresh cartridge, and as the bolt closes into the chamber so the continuing movement of the carrier revolves it to lock. At this moment the chain link we have been following has reached the front corner of the receiver, so the movement of the carrier stops and the round is fired. There is now a slight pause while the chain crosses the front of the receiver, which permits the shell to leave the bore and the chamber pressure to drop, and now the chain is moving rearwards to open the breech and start the cycle all over again.

There is obviously more detail than that; there has to be synchronous movement of the ammunition feed, and precise release of the firing pin, but these are mechanical details easily accommodated and driven from the external power supply – usually a 24 volt motor. The point is that the track of the chain, and its consequences, gives the gun an ideal working cycle since there is sufficient 'dwell' during the bolt closure to take care of ignition idiosyncracies and most hangfires, and even if there is a total misfire then the chain proceeds on its way and extracts the dud and ejects it.

The 20 mm having been successfully manufactured, Hughes then turned to a 30 mm design, completed the first prototype in four months, and successfully fired that. After the usual delays and conferences, committees and boards, the Chain Gun was accepted and has since been installed in a number of different helicopters.

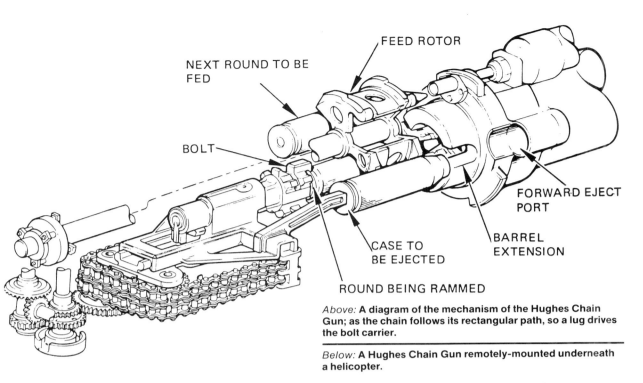

NEXT ROUND TO BE FED

FEED ROTOR

BOLT

FORWARD EJECT PORT

CASE TO BE EJECTED

BARREL EXTENSION

ROUND BEING RAMMED

Above: **A diagram of the mechanism of the Hughes Chain Gun; as the chain follows its rectangular path, so a lug drives the bolt carrier.**

Below: **A Hughes Chain Gun remotely-mounted underneath a helicopter.**

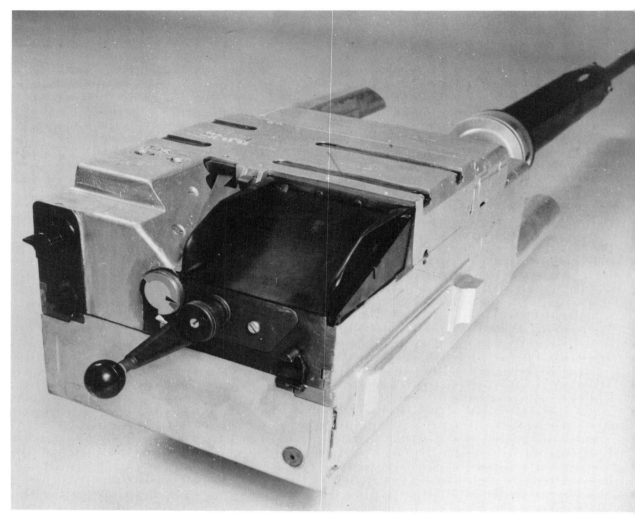

The British 30 mm Rarden cannon, a semi-automatic gun of extremely high accuracy.

The object of putting such a weapon in a helicopter was so that it could fire at ground targets, notably light and heavy armoured vehicles. By the late 1960s armour was becoming a major preoccupation; not only were there a lot of main battle tanks in the Warsaw Pact, but they also had a vast number of things like armoured personnel carriers, reconnaissance tanks and infantry fighting vehicles, all wearing some degree of armour. It followed that Western reconnaissance vehicles needed something which could deal with this sort of light armoured opponent; until then reconnaissance vehicles were generally satisfied with a medium machine gun, but this was no longer in the running.

And so in the early 1970s the cannon began to make an appearance on small armoured vehicles. One of the first to be designed was the British Rarden 30 mm, something of an oddity because it is not an automatic weapon, but a semi-automatic – an overgrown self-loading rifle if you like. The reasoning – which is hard to

fault – was that an accurate gun hardly needs to send a stream of shells at its opponent, and, moreover, if discarding sabot ammunition was used – as was intended – then it would be too expensive to blast off by the beltful. So a rapid succession of single shots would be just as effective and a good deal cheaper on both ammunition and barrels. (In fact the final design did have an automatic capability but it is rarely used).

The Rarden was designed around some very stringent requirements, the principal one of which was that it had to fit inside the turret of the forthcoming Fox armoured car and still leave enough room for the crew to operate. This led to some enormous engineering problems which took time to overcome, but the result was an amazingly accurate weapon with an inboard length of no more than 18 inches. Moreover all the operation of the breech takes place inside the receiver casing and the empty cases are ejected forward, down a tube, so that no fumes enter the turret. The operation of the Rarden sounds deceptively simple: the gun fires and the gun and breech recoil into the receiver. Towards the end of the recoil stroke the

Twin 25 mm cannon in a turret, complete with radar and optronic sight, forms a highly mobile and effective anti-aircraft system. (*Electronique Serge Dassault***)**

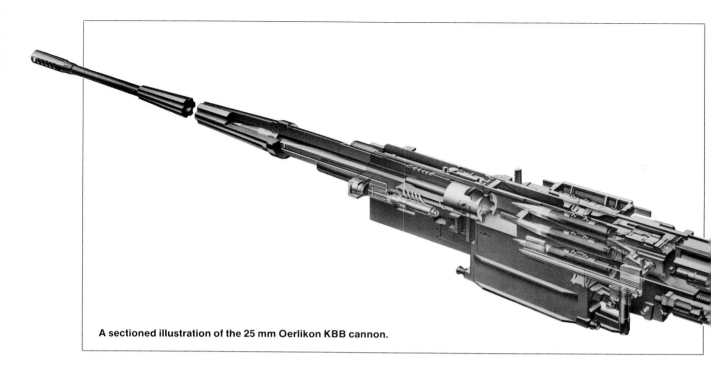

A sectioned illustration of the 25 mm Oerlikon KBB cannon.

horizontal sliding breech block slides open and an extractor grips the cartridge case. As the gun runs back into battery so the case is stripped from the chamber and ejected. A rammer then rams the next round in as the gun comes to rest and the breech closes. It sounds simple but, in the words of one senior officer concerned with the development 'The design is worth a Doctorate any day'.

In the wake of the Rarden came a host of cannon fitted to light armoured vehicles, with Oerlikon designs well to the fore. At the same time the sudden interest in cannon brought them back into the air defence role, largely because it was now possible to develop small surveillance radars and computer-aided electro-optical sights which took up little space but added enormously to the gun's ability to hit. Small turrets carrying radar, sights and twin cannon appeared on every sort of wheeled and tracked chassis and were widely adopted in many armies.

It will be remembered that the Germans, in 1942 or thereabouts, had arrived at the conclusion that the 20 mm shell was no longer good enough to defeat aircraft. This opinion had been reversed in postwar years by the development of better types of ammunition, but by the end of the 1960s it was becoming obvious that the 20 mm really had come to the end of its potential. Aircraft were wearing armour capable of stopping most types of 20 mm round, but designers were reluctant to move up to 30 mm since it meant proportionally large vehicles to carry the guns and their ammunition. The obvious answer was to look half-way, and so the 25 mm calibre began to appear. This allows a sizeable cartridge, giving

ample velocity for a flat trajectory and good hit probability, and a shell which is sufficiently improved over the 20 mm to give a considerable increase in lethality without going to extremes of size. Other 'median' calibres are the Soviet 23 mm, used with aircraft and air defence guns, and the German 27 mm developed for the cannon used with the Tornado aircraft.

In 1983 a new design appeared in France; the French had developed a number of conventional gas-operated cannon and also several revolver guns, but they now approached the externally-powered idea. The GIAT 25 mm Model 811 uses a novel camshaft drive to actuate a reciprocating bolt. Alongside the receiver is a rotating shaft with a cam groove, and engaged in this groove is a lug attached to the bolt carrier. As the shaft revolves so the carrier is driven back and forth, opening and closing the bolt, and gearing from the shaft drives the ammunition feed in synchrony. By varying the speed of the electric motor, by switching resistances in and out of circuit, the gun can be made to fire at 150, 400 or 650 rounds per minute. The Model 811 was followed by the Model 781 in 30 mm calibre. This uses a similar mechanism but has the rate of fire infinitely variable from single shots to 750 rounds per minute.

With the increasing application of cannon to ground targets, there came a demand for rapid changes in ammunition. If, for example, the cannon was loaded with anti-personnel high explosive shells and a tank hove into view, the gunner would need to open up, remove the belt, insert a fresh one loaded with armour-piercing ammunition, close the gun, recock it, and then

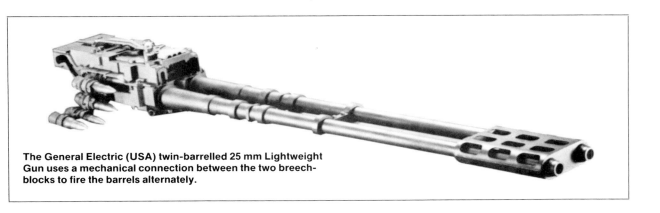

The General Electric (USA) twin-barrelled 25 mm Lightweight Gun uses a mechanical connection between the two breech-blocks to fire the barrels alternately.

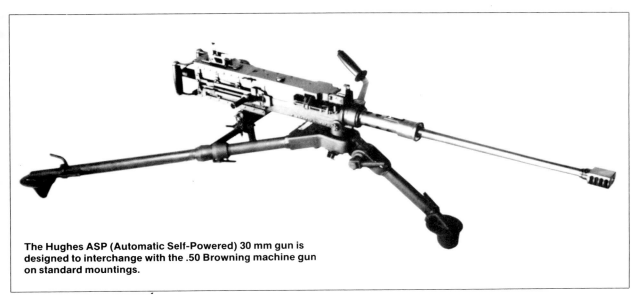

The Hughes ASP (Automatic Self-Powered) 30 mm gun is designed to interchange with the .50 Browning machine gun on standard mountings.

prepare to fire, by which time the target might have taken matters into its own hands. The solution to this seems to have first appeared in an American gun developed for the 'Bushmaster' project in the early 1960s: the Thomson-Ramo-Wooldridge design incorporated dual feed, with two belts entering the gun but only one actually feeding. By a quick movement of a lever one belt was thrown out of engagement and the other aligned with the feedway, so that the ammunition could be changed instantly. The Bushmaster project fell through when the Vietnam war ended and was not revived for some time. In the interim TRW sold their designs to Oerlikon and, after some changes, it reappeared as the Oerlikon KBA, still with dual feed. Since then the idea has been widely adopted and, in truth, it is unlikely that any cannon without dual feed would receive much of a hearing today.

Two more designs have recently appeared in the USA. The first is a two-barrelled gun from General Electric which is based on a design almost as old as the cannon idea. The 25 mm GE Lightweight Gun has

revived the German Gast mac'iine gun of 1918. The principle, put simply, is to have two barrels and bolts side-by-side in the same receiver. One bolt goes forward to load and fire; as it does so a cross-connecting lever forces the other bolt to the rear. When the gun fires the bolt runs back, and the lever forces the other bolt forward to load and fire. And so it goes on, the firing of one barrel providing the motive power to operate the other bolt. The motive power can be provided by gas piston, or by recoil, or even from an external power source; the design is flexible in this respect. The advantage is that with two barrels firing at 1000 rounds per minute each, we have a gun firing at 2000 rpm without overheating.

The second design is extremely interesting, less for its mechanical arrangements than for its potential tactical applications. The Hughes ASP (Automatic Self Powered) 30 mm gun moves away from the external power system of the Chain Gun and adopts a conventional gas piston operating system. By using a muzzle brake and recoil absorbers the recoil blow is reduced and the gun has been designed so that it can be interchanged on any existing mounting with the .50 Browning machine gun. Weighing 105 lbs and giving single shots or automatic fire up to 500 rpm, it is thus a possible ground gun for infantry support, but firing a useful 30 mm projectile. It is, in fact, chambered for the 30 mm Aden/DEFA cartridge which is in wide use throughout the world and in American service as the M789 series. Thus the gun uses an existing NATO-standard round, interchanges with a NATO-standard machine gun on a NATO-standard mount, and promises to give infantry a highly versatile weapon for either ground use of air defence.

One last design deserves mention, the Spanish Meroka. This is a reversion to the 'volley gun' of the middle 19th century in some respects, being a block of 12 barrels in two banks of six. A separate belt feeds ammunition to each bank of barrels, and a breech mechanism loads all the barrels at once and then fires them in a volley of six double shots. After firing the empty cases are withdrawn into the feed belt, the breech unit opens and the belts are moved six steps to present a fresh set of rounds to the multiple breeches. The breechblock chambers the new rounds and the gun is

ready to fire once more. In fact the next volley is fired automatically. The volley is fired in 0.06 second, and reloading takes 0.2 second; for mathematical reasons we need not go into, the rate of fire depends upon the number of volleys, three volleys being fired at 3724 rounds per minute. Meroka is produced in 20 mm and 30 mm calibres and is used extensively by the Spanish Navy as an air defence system, and it has considerable possibilities as a land service weapon.

In little more than a decade, therefore, the automatic cannon has moved from being basically an air service weapon to being a ground army weapon of considerable tactical value. As an arm for light vehicles it has excellent armour-piercing potential, though, to be fair, it is perhaps less effective as an infantry supporting weapon due to the flat trajectory and small projectile. On a ground mounting, as demonstrated by the Hughes ASP, it has the potential to replace the existing heavy machine gun and grenade launcher with a weapon which can do the same job as either of them but at even greater ranges. It has also begun to appear on tanks as a coaxial weapon, again replacing the rifle-calibre machine gun. The soldier of tomorrow will, truly, have cannon to right of him, cannon to left of him, cannon all round him.

Fighting in Built-Up Areas

Ernest Wood

Fighting in built-up areas has been a feature of warfare in both conventional and terrorist campaigns since the war. The level of intensity may vary from the sniper to the artillery barrage and air bombardment, but once the soldier is on the street (or better in the building, unseen by his opposition) many of the basic principles hold true.

Soviet troops combine fitness training with house-to-house combat training in a highly practical manner.

A German MG 34 machine gun in the sustained fire role in a street of a Soviet town. In this role the MG 34 could be used to hit point targets like windows at long ranges. (*IWM*)

To some readers the subject of FIBUA – Fighting in Built-up Areas, or the less euphonious MOUT – Military Operations in Urban Terrain (the latter is a US Army term) is all about the Second World War. FIBUA is the stuff of Stalingrad and Berlin, and has only recently been rediscovered in Beirut. However, closer examination will show that soldiers and resistance groups have been fighting in cities and towns from 1945 to 1986.

The Korean war saw action in Seoul, while the Hungarian uprising and the Anglo French landings in Egypt in 1956 led to fighting in Budapest and Suez. Beirut has been a battlefield in 1958, 1975 – 1978 and then most dramatically in 1982 with the Israeli invasion of the Lebanon. In that year there was also fighting in the refugee camps along the coast which was slow and costly compared to the high speed wars fought by the Israelis in the past. The US invaded Dominica in 1965 and fought in the streets of San Domingo. Vietnam was a battle ground with the Tet offensive of 1968 and here Hue, Saigon and Kontum saw intense but localised fighting. At the close of US involvement in Vietnam there was fighting in Quang Tri City and An Loc in 1972 and finally in 1975 the South fell to Northern armour with fighting in Xuan Loc and Saigon.

The cities of Northern Ireland have had their share of trouble in the 1970s and urban riots and ambush and sniping were also a problem in many a major city in the west in the years since the end of the war.

FIBUA in NATO

It has become a widely accepted view that the increase of urban development and the spread of suburbs and light industry have made parts of West Germany a brick and concrete anti-tank obstacle. Such attitudes declared that the Ardennes were proof against German armour in 1940 – the exact words of the French General who spoke of the Ardennes were that they were tank proof 'if defended'. The same holds true of urban areas. Undefended they are no real obstacle – every year NATO exercises rumble through German towns and villages, and the by-pass and freeway make cities no obstacle to a motorist in a hurry.

Defended however, even a small village can become a strong point. Analysis of exercises in Germany has shown that the two to three kilometer distance between villages makes them ideal as mutually supporting anti-tank bastions with Milan reaching out to hit Warsaw Pact armour as it exposes its flanks or rear moving by road or cross country.

However urban fighting requires a special sort of soldier. Many of the major battles of the Second World War were fought by men toughened by years of war and training.

A level of independence and firm and intelligent leadership at section level is required to make soldiers who may be familiar with operations in open country, effective in the unfamiliar environment of a West German city. A rather grim insight into these problems was a conversation that the author had with a West German who had served as a young soldier at the end of the war. When he was asked whether fortifying a German home would not have its owner almost up in arms against the soldiers – or the inhabitants of a defended village faced with destruction by Soviet artillery would attempt to eject the NATO soldiers, the German replied, 'If a man came between you and your means of staying alive – you would kill him'. Stalingrad was not fought by men who wanted to disappear into the 'Cauldron' and there are reports of Political Commissars shooting men reluctant to cross the river to join fighting on the west bank of the Volga.

Though Western training manuals cover operations underground – in sewers, cellars and sub-way and underground systems – this is a field of operations that is even more testing than conventional FIBUA on the surface.

With these caveats let us take a closer look at urban warfare. It is an axiom of war that ground of tactical value must be held or covered. Thus a well built building in a minor suburb may be a superb position to defend, but of no tactical value. The defence of such an area would be as disruptive to enemy movement as a sniper holing up in a suburban house – if he wants to have an effect the sniper should get a firing position where he can dominate important ground and hit valuable targets. Lee Harvey Oswald in the Book Depository at Dallas had a clear view of President Kennedy. Oswald was in a building dominating key ground.

Solid Houses and Homes

Modern building techniques have produced well insulated and easy to construct homes and public buildings. Some have a steel girder frame with thin walls with glass and plaster board. The author has seen a GPMG gunner chop down a breeze block wall with a series of short bursts of fire. If 7.62 mm rounds can do this then clearly heavier weapons can destroy buildings, or render them uninhabitable very quickly. The ideal construction is a turn of the century factory or public building. Massive stone or brick constructions have also been reinforced with a steel girder frame – with less knowledge of the load bearing qualities of steel and concrete some of these buildings had the extra precaution of brick arches between each girder.

A large building offers upper floors that may collapse under shell fire but which will remain supported by other floors. US television crews in Beirut were reported to have taken the upper floors of hotel blocks – this put

The light anti-tank gun played a valuable part in the street fighting during the Second World War, as seen here on the approaches to Stalingrad. Today its place has been taken by the rocket launcher and light recoilless gun.

them out of range of accurate small arms fire, but under two protective floors.

The US Army define built-up areas as Residential Sprawl; Core Periphery; Outlying Industrial Areas; Outlying Highrise Areas; City Core and Commercial Ribbon. Each of these areas has its own peculiar buildings and configurations. Some are ideal for defence, while others made from very light pre-fabricated units only offer cover from view.

The buildings can be broken down into two groups – Mass Buildings and Framed Buildings. The former include massive stone or brick structures and 'wall and slab' buildings like factories. The latter have a girder frame with a light or heavy cladding – either brick or concrete, or a light insulated material.

The techniques become more complex when the soldier looks at street widths and the angles at which he can see in or out of windows or loop holes.

Finally there are the sewers and underground railways. Combat in this black and claustrophobic environment is protrayed in the Polish film *Kanal* which covers the attempts of a resistance group to escape from the Germans in 1944 after the Warsaw Rising. However, men who are prepared to enter sewers and cellars can launch raids and counter-attacks behind enemy lines, or evade capture. Clearly any unit that is embarking on the defence or assault of a built-up area needs to look at the maps, aerial photographs and most importantly the local government plans of services like power, gas and sewage conduits.

Defending a House

In the British All Arms tactics manual there is a diagram of a rather attractive villa that has been prepared for defence. With the passage of time the house has changed its character from the respectable 1940s house that was first portrayed. However many of the lessons in this diagram still hold true. Not least is that the defenders keep back from the windows, even though this can lead to a smaller arc of fire. The basic structure of the house is reinforced with sandbags and glass removed from windows. Curtains however are retained since they give some cover from view. The doors are blocked and stairs either removed or blocked with wire. For the defenders the access and egress is via 'mouseholes' – small holes cut in the walls of neighbouring houses while movement between floors is by ladder and holes in ceilings. Floors are sandbagged against machine gun fire, but a hole can be left to allow grenades to be dropped on those below.

Fire is a major problem, as the defenders of the bridge at Arnhem discovered in 1944. Thus either earth, sand or water should be available. However water will be at premium as the mains will be cut or polluted. The defenders should switch their power off at the mains, but one veteran of Beirut suggests that bare live cables in houses likely to be occupied by the opposition can be used as an extra hazard. Another approach to FIBUA from Beirut is to fortify only the outer face of a building – thus as you retreat to another defended building your

Light air defence weapons have a useful secondary role in built-up areas. While their primary task is to keep the enemy away, their high rate of fire make them into useful direct support guns.

A British platoon commander in a village in Normandy in June 1944, with the 2-inch mortar ready to hand to fire smoke cover for further movement. (*IWM*)

opposition finds that your former strong point offers them no protection from fire from positions sited in greater depth.

For most armies there is a hope that they will live to fight another day, so an exit is essential for the sake of morale. However positions should be constructed so that they will withstand heavy close range fire.

The use of barbed wire and the destruction of external features of a building may draw attention to it, so other buildings must be treated in a similar way. One solution is to fabricate shell damage so that random holes can be used to disguise loop holes, and rubble to conceal reinforcement. It is perhaps ironic that the easier it is for a soldier to cut a loop hole in a wall – the easier it is also for enemy small arms or artillery to destroy the defender or the building. Preparing a building for defence, like digging a trench with proper top cover is hard work – anything less is pointless.

Some weapons like anti-tank or automatic weapons have distinctive signatures and care must be taken that they either do not kick up so much dust that they catch the eye of their target, or that back blast does not injure the crew. Some anti-tank weapons have a very small back blast and thus can be used either in tank hunting patrols or in ambush and defence.

Attack

Though the defender has many advantages in an urban battlefield, the attacker can be successful with the right combination of arms and tactics.

One of the first needs for an attacker is to know what he holds and where the enemy are still in control. This can literally be the difference between upstairs and downstairs. Some FIBUA drills call for the use of chalk to mark which rooms are clear. Friendly aircraft also need to know where the 'bomb line' begins and marker pannels, flags or smoke can be used. Air mobility has made FIBUA a more fluid and faster form of warfare than the 1940s and 1950s. Helicopters can be used to put men on top of high rise buildings, or to take them deep into enemy held areas of the city without the dangerous business of moving along streets.

The use of armour in FIBUA has always been seen as a double edged weapon. While the tank can be used to destroy enemy positions and give powerful direct fire support, it is also very vulnerable when closed down and needs a good infantry escort. One of the advantages of direct fire – either from tanks, SP guns or the weapons mounted on an APC is that they can be used to create an entrance for infantry to assault a building. If they are not available the soldiers will need to use an anti-tank weapon (however this makes a small hole) or a frame charge. This consists of a simple wooden frame with explosives fixed to it – the most memorable example of its use recently was the SAS assault on the Iranian Embassy in London. Once the charge has exploded the assault group must rush into the building before the defenders have enough time to recover from the noise and blast. The use of automatic fire and grenades and fast violent action will retain the initiative as the men work their way through the building. Ideally the building should be cleared from above – grenades can be thrown downstairs with greater ease.

The breaching charges can also be used to blast through walls into neighbouring houses and thus a terrace or block can be cleared without men emerging onto exposed roads or gardens.

Flame throwers, either man-pack or vehicle mounted can be used – flame can be bounced off walls to hit positions that are behind cover. The flame weapon is also effective against well defended positions where it can be used to burn off the oxygen and suffocate the defenders.

FIBUA is very costly in men and will consume large amounts of ammunition. In the assault stretcher bearers can be used to bring ammunition forward and move casualities back – however if they are used in this role they cannot work with the protection of the Red Cross when moving ammunition.

A French-manned American .30-cal Browning machine gun in action in the ruins of Karlsruhe at the close of the Second World War. (*SCA*)

127

The Terrorist Battle Ground

Urban terrorism and the use of paramilitary and military forces in a peace-time environment has led to a re-evaluation of tactics. Soldiers have been on the streets with rifles before the troubles in Belfast – the siege of Sydney Street before the First World War saw greatcoated Guardsmen with their bolt-action rifles covering a house in which armed anarchists had taken refuge.

The principle of minimum force which has been the policy of most operations by Western democratic governments can lead to delays and thus greater publicity for the terrorist who has taken up a gun, but it can also save lives. One of the problems that soldiers have faced is that they are not by nature or training believers in minimum force. Conventional war demands a maximum effort and any weapon or tactic that destroys the enemy or his will to fight it brought to bear. In a busy street in a city in peace time a random rifle round can penetrate walls and kill or disable people who have no part in the violence on the streets.

The British Army has over the years developed an elaborate training programme for men who are due to serve in Northern Ireland. Soldiers have to be able to identify the location of a single rifle shot; while in a rural environment the 'crack and thump' of the shot will give some indication of range, and whether the man is under direct fire, in a city this can be lost in a jumble of noise and echoes.

Attacks on security forces can be made using remotely-fired bombs in which the operator is well away from the target and can be alerted by observers who blend as part of the urban crowd. To counter this patrols adopt random patterns. Buildings are screened from small arms and rocket fire, though home-made mortars can be used by terrorists to lob bombs into the police or army bases.

One of the less apparent features of urban terrorism and street violence is the way in which the security forces can become familiar with the men they are hunting. The sniper or bomber may be known by name – his photograph may exist though he is seldom likely to resemble it; however like Mao's fish in the water the terrorist will blend in and be protected by fear or favour by the civilian population.

To win this variety of street fighting requires initiative at a very low level. It is a Corporal's war – like conventional FIBUA the section and its commander with their narrow front and small area of responsibility are a key unit. However in the terrorist war the Section and its commander can also be on nationwide television by the evening if they make a false move and make or

Smoke and dust envelops a building in Kehl in 1945 – some of the hazards of street fighting. (SCA)

129

A British patrol waiting outside a German village during a recent exercise. A small reconnaissance party has entered the village to see if there is any opposition.

take casualties. The British Army has been served very well by its Corporals since the beginning of the troubles in 1970. The terrorist war is also about politics and when this author visited Belfast in 1985 the Army was alert to the Noraid visit by pro-Provisional IRA Americans.

The Home Service Force

The Home Guard in 1940 developed considerable expertise in local defence of their community against a potential German invasion. Pill boxes built at key points and patrols in areas that were regarded as possible parachute dropping zones kept the UK defences at a high level of readiness and released the younger regular soldiers for service in Africa and the Far East.

The Home Service Force has been dubbed a Dad's Army after the Home Guard of the 1940s. It is a

The 84 mm Carl Gustav anti-tank weapon crewed by men of the 4th Battalion the Royal Green Jackets. The Carl Gustav can be used to blast enemy positions in the assault as well as killing tanks. (*4 RGJ*)

misnomer since the role is different. However, though the HSF guard Key Points and in the recent Brave Defender Exercise were reported to have won 'on points', the Home Guard and the HSF have a number of strengths in common. The greatest is local knowledge; this not only allows them to identify strangers and possible intruders and saboteurs, but also to know the local geography. Local knowledge is a very valuable asset in the brief and violent contacts that may follow a special forces assault.

We may not see the splendid little pamphlets produced by Colonel G. A. Wade MC in the Second World War being used for training – he covered *The Defence of Houses*, *The Defence of Villages and Small Towns* and *The Defence of Towns* – but his vigorous attitude to urban operations in the UK homeland which was headed 'Wanted a Sense of Reality' may remain the touchstone for Home Service training and planning.

The Death of Sergeant York

Hugh Lucas

Swiss Oerlikon-Buhrle ADATS (air defence anti-tank system) shown here installed on a M113A2 APC during trials in the USA.

When military and civilian officials' careers are at stake, it is easy to overlook the fact that a new weapons system lacks about half the range to carry out its mission. And it does not hurt to have someone with at least passing familiarity with the contractor in a decision-making position. Those are two of the major features of the after-the-battle report on the killing of Sergeant York, the US Army's Divisional Air Defense System (DIVADS) gun, which Defense Secretary Casper W. Weinberger ordered junked on 27 August after months of indecision and political jockeying. 'We wound up losing $1.8 billion (the amount already expended in research and production) but we're not going to lose any American boys because of it' said one of those opposing the Sgt York system in the Pentagon. He was referring to the fact that DIVADS had demonstrated a range of,

British Aerospace Dynamics Laserfire surface-to-air missile system shown here mounted on a Bedford MK (4 ×4) 4-tonner truck chassis.

at best, four kilometres, while its prospective opponent in battle, the Soviet Hind E combat helicopter, armed with an AT-6 missile, could stand off six kilometres.

What made the Army's continuation of the programme for so long so incredible was that it was well aware of the situation. In answer to the specific question of whether the DIVADS gun had adequate range to counter the AT-6, the service had this to say:

'Yes. Originally the specified range of the Sgt York was able to counter most of the range of the AT-6 missile. This would have greatly reduced the effectiveness of the Soviet AT-6-armed attack helicopter by forcing it to engage targets at extended ranges. At an extended range, even with good visibility, targets would be difficult to locate, identify and, if moving, to maintain a line of sight from the helicopter long enough to guide a missile to intercept. Studies showed that this missile range "advantage" was not practically exploitable, particularly since the battle is rarely one-on-one, and the

helicopter will rarely know his position relative to the Sgt York guns with precision'.

And one of the officials authorising such statements was James R. Ambrose, Undersecretary of the Army, the Number Two position in the civilian hierarchy. He had taken the job after retiring from the Ford Motor Company and its subsidiary, Ford Aerospace and Communications Corporation, the manufacturer of Sgt York. When the question of a possible conflict of interest had arisen, Ambrose sought advice from Darrell L. Peck, the service's deputy general counsel for military and civil affairs.

He surveyed Ambrose's various benefits from the company, such as a fixed-amount pension that did not depend upon Ford earnings; a free goup life insurance policy; another group health policy which he partly paid and Ford paid the rest; and 'an option to lease up to two automobiles from Ford at rates lower than those available to the public'. Peck concluded that his boss was not required to 'sign a statement disqualifying yourself from acting on any matters affecting Ford Motor Co or its subsidiaries' as a result of receiving these retirement benefits.

133

The whole of this furor arose from a US Army desire to achieve a more effective air defence weapon than its ageing Vulcan 20 mm multiple-barrel cannon. It drafted a Required Operational Capability (ROC) document in 1976, issued Requests for Proposals (RFPs) the following year, and signed contracts in 1978 with Ford and with General Dynamics Corporation's Pomona, California, Division. The latter company offered an armament subsystem using two NATO-standard 35 mm Oerlikon KDA cannon with independent linked-belt feed systems, with a fire control system based on the Phalanx Close-in Weapons System featuring a search-and-track radar with separate antennae, Identification Friend or Foe (IFF) equipment, and a day-night electro-optical sight with integrated laser rangefinder.

The Ford entry, which received an initial $159.2 million awards on 7 May 1981, for three years of production options totalling 276 systems, used the Westinghouse search-and-track radar derived from the AN/APG-66 model used in the early versions of the F-16 fighter aircraft, twin Bofors L/70 40 mm guns and ammunition, and a Ford-developed linkless ammunition feed system.

Both weapon systems were mounted on modified M48A5 tank chassis, as part of an effort to utilise proven systems so as to provide lower costs and reduced development time. But however commendable that might appear on paper, the end result was that the melange of equipment actually contributed to the problem. The situation moved James P. Wade Jr, the Assistant Secretary of Defense for Acquisition and Logistics, to say at the funeral news conference for Sgt York, 'I think we need to go back and reflect in some detail, but certainly a lesson learned here is (the assumption) that the application of sub-systems that have been proven in other mission areas will thereby work in another mission area by putting them together into a new system. I think we're going to learn a lesson there. We've got to be careful about that approach'.

The 'merely-fitting-the-pieces-together' concept also figured in the other major problem of DIVADS – concurrent research and development and production. The Pentagon incessantly gives lip-service to the 'fly-before-buy' approach favoured by former Deputy Defense Secretary David Packard, and just as continuously finds ways to rationalise violating it. And Wade continued in that tradition by telling Pentagon reporters 'Every weapons system has its own acquisition strategy. We will not turn off concurrency just because of the example of DIVADS. You have to look at it in the light of the pieces that go into a weapons system. I think in this case the lesson learned was that certainly over-optimism in the context of taking sub-systems that were proven in other areas and putting them together in a new integrated system having a different application ...

Thomson-CSF Crotale surface-to-air missile system used by many countries. In this photograph a missile is being launched from one of the firing units with acquisition system on right.

Euromissile Roland 2 surface-to-air missile system, 27 of which are already in service with the US Army's National Guard shown here on a M812A1 5-ton 6 × 6 truck.

there was an over-optimism in the context of that being part of the production decision to go forward, and go forward in the context of when you will actually test the programme'.

Wade also appeared to downgrade the possibility that the follow-on to DIVAD, whose mission the Army still considers vital, would be a missile system in order to overcome the range deficiencies for defending against Soviet helicopter gunships. He noted that even without Sgt York the Army will have 'plenty of guns on the battlefield ... to include those guns on the fighting vehicle, the Bradley has a 25 mm gun and that gun can be brought to bear against aircraft'. He said that the cancellation does not mean there will be a decision against using guns against 'tactical ingressing aircraft or helicopters'.

During the entire development/production process the Army has taken a similar hard-headed stance, insisting that each test phase had proved the weapon was satisfactory in all but one or two areas and that there was strong confidence the difficulties would easily be overcome. And the term 'hard-headed' may be an excessively polite one. At one point, after the Army had been scheduled to fire 15,000 rounds and drive the tank chassis over 4,000 miles of varying terrain it reported to an enquiry by the press and Congress that the number of events were less than planned. It was learned later that the service had fired 3,600 rounds and, because of repeated equipment breakdowns, was able to conduct only 300 miles of road-testing.

The Army also made certain that newsmen were provided with a report that DIVADS had '... successfully engaged and shot down' four QH-50 sub-scale helicopter targets at the Dona Ana Test Range at Fort Bliss, Texas. Unfortunately, during that period guns being fired by Sen Alan Dixon, Illinois Democrat, jammed during the demonstration and were unable to be repaired. The Army later blamed the senator for failing to flip a safety switch when it was decided to change from practice rounds to live ammunition, causing the system to turn itself off.

The system had also been denigrated for undergoing unrealistic testing, including one reported incident when a radar picked up a latrine fan which it apparently thought was a helicopter's rotor blade turning, and so tracked and acquired it. Lieut-General Louis C. Wagner, Deputy Chief-of-Staff for Research, Development & Acquisition, strongly denied that story, saying that it 'has taken on a life of its own and few in the media seem to know or care that it is false'.

General Wagner also said that during at least one test Sgt York had been fired at a 'stationary non-flyable helicopter used to simulate a low-flying helicopter' but, he claimed, that was a test of the ammunition. For hovering helicopters the radar depended upon the symmetrical doppler return from the rotating parts for detection and tracking; but in another test the turbine engine of the target machine had been removed and two electric motors were used to drive the rotor. 'Using these motors the normal rotor speed could not be achieved,' Wagner said. 'The low rotor speed coupled with the helicopter having only two blades (as against the five blades of the Soviet Hind helicopter) made it necessary to augment the target helicopter with Luneberg lenses. The installation and use of radar augmentation is an acceptable practice in both developmental and operational testing'. He was not asked why, in view of these circumstances, the test was held at all.

The Army also claimed that it had demonstrated successes against remotely-controlled F-100 drones and UH-1 simulated gunships. However, it turned out that in one case the F-100 made 18 passes across the firing area before being hit, the Huey helicopters were unable to hover, and that the targets were blown up anyway, by remote control, after the cannons had fired. The Army said that the destruction was a matter of safey, to prevent the targets flying outside the test range boundaries. Besides, it said, proximity-fuzed ammunition was adjudged by test officials to have come close enough to be effective.

But the Army was determined not to be swayed by any doubts that the test procedures might arouse. It said in a 'discussion paper' issued to officers with media contacts that 'DIVAD has demonstrated its effectiveness against manoeuvring fixed-wing targets and against its primary threat, the hovering helicopter. It meets our expectations regarding engagement of moving targets and identification of friend or foe. The Sgt York is capable of performing its roles of support to manoeuvre forces and convoy protection as an integrated part of a combined arms force. The live fire performance of the system against ground targets, a secondary role, meets our expectations at reasonable combat ranges'.

The only problem, the paper said, was that it took too long to clear an armament stoppage. But, it told media information officials, 'To date, the frequency of occurence of such incidents has been acceptably low'.

But Congress, which has become an increasingly prominent actor in dramas of this sort, was not about to let itself be subverted by the facts, especially not Senator Barry Goldwater, a former Presidential candidate as a Republican from Arizona who was defeated in large part because of his image as a man with his finger on the nuclear trigger. He said that an Armed Services Committee hearing over which he presided was occasioned by 'the inaccurate "hatchet job" by the press' on DIVADS. He said the system's problems were caused primarily by the attempt to shorten the developmental cycle and indicated that he felt the temporary halt to the programme, ordered in the autumn of 1984 by Defense Secretary Weinberger for follow-on evaluation, was un-needed. 'I think the Secretary of Defense has made a bad decision based on a misleading and sensational newspaper story. I'm behind the DIVAD and I hope Weinberger's decision does not kill the program'.

Pressure on Weinberger came from another direction, however, when several Congressmen, who are not noted for failing to beat their breasts when it suits their purpose, threatened him with impeachment if he did not cancel DIVADS. The smell of blood also brought in pressure from other armament manufacturers with their own legislative and public constituency to fill the vacuum for a system the Army admittedly vitally requires.

Lest anyone think the Pentagon hierarchy was chagrined by casting away $1.8 billion for a system that would have cost, at minimum, $3 billion more, here is Wade at the 27 August news conference:
'We made a tough decision in the sense of where the program was, and when you have to make a tough decision in where the monies are that can be saved, and whether you want to continue with that programme ... certainly you would agree that if we had an unlimited amount of money we might well have continued with the programme'.

So much for lessons learned.

Since this article was written a Forward Area Air Defense Working Group was established and early in December 1985 had settled on five missile system candidates to replace DIVAD. We have taken the opportunity to illustrate this article with a selection of these systems.

As this issue went to press it was reported that a gun/missile system was to be the preferred choice.

The Argentine Ground Forces in the Falklands War

Adrian J. English

Understandably, most English language accounts of the Falklands War have concentrated on the role of the British Armed Forces. Although the achievements of the Argentine Air Force and Naval Aviation have received due credit, little has appeared in print regarding the role of the Argentine Army and Marines which, if undistinguished, was in reality far better than contemporary accounts would indicate, bearing in mind that Argentina had not fought a foreign war for 112 years and that the troops which faced them – Guards, Ghurkas, SAS, Paratroops and Royal Marines – were the elite of one of the world's finest armies, with a history of almost continuous combat experience since the Second World War. Almost four years after the event, it is interesting to study the activities of the Argentine ground forces in the South Atlantic War.

The landing; Royal Marines of the Port Stanley garrison being disarmed.

Although the story of the invasion is now widely known, much confusion has arisen concerning the actual units which took part.

On 27 March, the submarine *Santa Fé* left its base at Mar del Plata with a contingent of the Buzo Táctico, the Argentine equivalent of the British Special Boat Service, aboard and sailed north-eastward. Two days later, ostensibly to take part in manoeuvres with the Uruguayan Navy, Task Force 20, comprising the aircraft carrier *Veinticinco de Mayo*, four old ex-US destroyers, a tanker and an armed tug, sailed northward towards the River Plate estuary from the main Argentine naval base of Puerto Belgrano, subsequently altering course south-eastward to rendezvous at sea with the *Santa Fé*.

Simultaneously, Task Force 40, comprising the modern destroyers *Hércules* and *Santísima Trinidad*, the frigates *Drummond* and *Granville*, the landing ship *Cabo San Antonio*, the transport *Isla de Los Estados* and the icebreaker *Almirante Irízar*, headed southward towards Puerto Deseado. Aboard this group were elements of the 2nd Infantry Battalion, the Amphibious Vehicles Battalion and the Amphibious Reconnaissance Company

Royal Marines being led off to captivity.

Two bemused citizens of Port Stanley regard an imposing array of Argentine amphibian vehicles.

An Argentine LVTP7 amphibian leading a patrol along the main street of Port Stanley.

of the Argentine Marine Corps, in all about 1200 men, with 13 LVTP7 and six LARC5 amphibious assault vehicles under the command of Rear-Admiral Carlos Busser.

Task Force 40 continued southward in the direction of Ushuaia before turning east. *Almirante Irízar* was detached to Puerto Deseado to pick up elements of the 25th Motorised Infantry Regiment and the 9th Motorised Engineer Company, both part of the IXth Motorised Infantry Brigade, with its HQ at Comodoro Rivadavia and which were designated as the permanent garrison of the Falklands after their conquest.

Both task forces reached the islands on 30 March, Task Force 40, standing off the north coast of the Archipelago while Task Force 20 was originally intended to circle the islands to the south carrying out

The Argentine commanders on a tour of inspection.

Left: **An Argentine Marine, commanding an LVTP7, celebrating victory.**

subsidiary landings at Darwin and Goose Green as well as a main assault on Stanley. Heavy weather caused a modification of the original plans to entail a concentration of the assault on Stanley alone.

The invasion began at 9.15 pm on 1 April when the destroyer *Santísima Trinidad* anchored off Port Harriet and disembarked 77 members of the Amphibious Reconnaissance Company into inflatable boats. These landed, without opposition, at Mullett Creek at 10.30 pm, rapidly securing Cape Pembroke lighthouse at the mouth of Stanley Harbour. Two companies of the 2nd Marines followed at midnight in landing craft from the *Cabo San Antonio*, fanning out to take the airport, the runways of which had been blocked by vehicles. A landing site had been chosen at a point on the south side of Stanley Harbour and at 2.00 am 15 frogmen of the

Buzo Táctico disembarked from the submarine *Santa Fé* at the mouth of the harbour to secure this objective.

The first LVTPs, carrying 200 men of the 25th Infantry Regiment, came ashore at 6.15 am, meeting light initial resistance before rolling on to link up with the group from the *Santísima Trinidad* together with whom they converged on Government House, where the main British resistance occurred. More or less simultaneously, 150 members of the 2nd Marines were landed from helicopters at Mullett Creek, a further force of 70, landed by helicopter, discovering that the Royal Marine barracks at Moody Brook was untenanted. At the same time a single Sea King Helicopter airlifted a platoon of the 9th Engineers from the *Almirante Irizar* to the now secure airport which was ready to receive the first Hercules transport aircraft at 8.30 am or 55 minutes before Governor Hunt and the 79 man Royal Marine garrison finally surrendered. Argentine losses in the operation were one dead and two wounded and an LVTP disabled.

A massive sea and air lift of personnel and equipment

between the mainland and Stanley was now mounted. After the surrender of the British garrison at Stanley, the remainder of the 25th Infantry Regiment and the 9th Engineer Company were flown in from the mainland, followed by the 8th Infantry Regiment and the IXth Brigade command. From 11 April onwards the IIIrd and Xth Motorised Infantry Brigades, based respectively at Curuzú-Cuatiá and Buenos Aires and comprising the 4th, 5th and 12th and the 3rd, 6th and 7th Infantry Regiments, with most of their supporting units, were also flown in.

The 601st Engineer Company, an army level unit, was also airlifted from the mainland and commenced the lengthening of the runway at Stanley airport by laying 200 feet of steel plating. A full system of lighting was also installed around the runway and parking bays so as to permit the use of the airport around the clock and work on the installation of arrester gear, to allow all-weather landing by naval Skyhawks and Super Etendards, also commenced although the latter work was never completed. Elements of the 601st and 101st Anti-Aircraft Artillery Groups, the former an army level unit, the later the major air defence unit of the 1st Army Corps, were brought in between 9 and 16 April, followed by the 601st Commando Company on 26 April.

The Argentine infantry regiments were in fact triangular battalions numbering from 500 to 900 men, the artillery groups approximating to regiments in British usage and the other units being of equivalent average strength to their British counterparts.

The Marine units which had carried out the assault were re-embarked and returned to the mainland during the first days following the invasion, being replaced by the 5th Marine Infantry Battalion from Rio Grande, reinforced with a company of the 3rd Marines, a field battery, an anti-aircraft battery and an engineer company.

The garrison of the islands was now deemed to have reached the maximum level which could be effectively supplied by airlift in the presence of the British sea blockade and the continuing tension with Chile over the Beagle Channel dispute also demanded that the elite mountain brigades stationed along the Argentino-Chilean frontier, whose training and equipment best suited them for operations in the climatic conditions of the Falklands, should be left intact and in position.

On the eve of the British re-invasion there were about 11,400 Argentine military personnel, including almost 2000 members of the Air Force and 1000 of the Navy and Marines in the Falkland archipelago. Brigadier General Mario Banjamín Menéndez, as Military Governor, exercised overall command of the Falklands garrison with Brigadier Generals Américo Daher and Oscar L. Jofre in operational command of the IXth and Xth Brigades respectively at Port Stanley.

A routine patrol, under the new flag.

An Argentine patrol moving through Port Stanley on a routine check.

Argentine troops, with a variety of weapons, celebrate the change of name from Falklands to Malvinas.

Digging in; a mortar position close to Port Stanley airfield.

Troops moving out of Port Stanley to take up blocking positions.

At or in the vicinity of Stanley were the three regiments of the Xth Motorised Infantry Brigade, minus their APCs; the 4th Infantry Regiment, many of whose members were already suffering the effects of their sudden transition from the sub-tropical climate of their normal station near the Brazilian frontier to the semi-Antarctic conditions of the Falklands in winter and the 25th Infantry Regiment. There were also the 601st and 602nd Commando Companies, the latter flown in on 29 May, the 601st Special Forces Squadron of the Argentine Gendarmerie, the 5th Marine Infantry Battalion, reinforced by a battery of six 105 mm howitzers and a Marine Engineer Company and elements of the 10th Armoured Cavalry Reconnaissance Squadron with ten Panhard AML 245 H-90 armoured cars. As the Falkland terrain consisted of a mixture of peat bog and mountain, no heavy armoured vehicles were transferred to the islands.

Artillery support was provided by the 3rd Artillery Group with three batteries, each comprising six OTO Melara Model 56 105 mm howitzers, reinforced with three Argentine-built CITEFA 155 mm howitzers detached from the 101st and 121st Artillery Groups and the 4th Ariborne Artillery Group, also comprising three six-gun batteries of 105 mm howitzers. There were also two six-gun batteries of twin 35 mm Oerlikon GDF-002 anti-aircraft guns plus one Roland and three Tigercat SAM units from the 601st Anti-Aircraft Defence Group, a battery of eight single 30 mm Hispano-Suiza pieces from the 101st AA Artillery Group and a battery of 12 similar weapons and three Tigercat SAM units of the 1st Marine Anti-Aircraft Regiment, in addition to the IInd Air Defence Squadron of the Argentine Air Force with nine twin-mounted 20 mm RH-202 guns. The infantry also had British Blowpipe and Soviet SA-7 man-portable SAM launchers, the latter provided by Peru.

Apart from logistic support and medical units, there were also the 10th Motorised Engineer Company and a company from the 601st Construction Engineer Battalion, together with a detachment from the 181st Military Police Intelligence Battalion. Most units having been transported to the islands without their organic transport, a lack of surface mobility bedevilled the Argentines throughout the campaign. In all there were 74 trucks of from 1/2 ton to 6 tons, three tanker trucks, eight ambulances and 75 jeeps, even the artillery lacking its own prime-movers.

147

Two Exocet launchers jury-rigged to a trailer and used as coast defence artillery to protect Port Stanley. One of these missiles damaged HMS *Glamorgan* some 20 km off-shore.

The Army had two Chinooks, two Pumas, three Agusta A109 and nine Bell UH-1H and D helicopters of the 601st Combat Aviation Battalion in the vicinity of Stanley. Two Chinooks and two Bell UH-1Hs of the Air Force were also available for additional air mobility.

After Stanley, the main concentration of Argentine forces was at Goose Green where the 12th Infantry, together with half of a 105 mm howitzer battery of the 4th Artillery Group and a section each of 35 mm and 20 mm AA pieces manned by the Air Force were deployed, together with about 200 Air Force personnel to operate the half dozen Pucará aircraft based at the air strip. In overall command was an Air Force officer, Air Vice-Commodore Wilson Pedrozo, the more numerous army elements being under the command of Lieutenant-Colonel Halo Pioggi.

Other points on East Falkland were covered by small outposts at not more than platoon strength, or by patrols, the latter mostly carried out by the Special Forces units.

There were also still about 120 air force and naval aviation personnel and a company of the 3rd Marines on Pebble Island although the value of this installation had greatly diminished after the raid on 12 May.

West Falkland was garrisoned by the 5th Infantry at Port Howard and the 8th Infantry plus the 9th Motorised Engineer Company at Fox Bay, the garrison being commanded by Brigadier General Omar Parada with his HQ at Port Howard. As on East Falkland, no major troop concentrations occurred outside these two centres, the remainder of the Island being covered by desultory patrols.

The only Argentine aircraft on West Falkland were three Army Puma and one Agusta 109 helicopters, based at Port Howard.

The British landings at San Carlos Bay went almost unopposed. Pre-war Argentine studies had dismissed San Carlos as a site for a landing and the settlement was garrisoned only by a reinforced platoon from the 12th Infantry Regiment. This small force retreated in the face of the invaders, shooting down two Royal Marine Gazelle helicopters as they withdrew.

During the landings a Chinook and two Army Pumas were destroyed on the ground at Mount Kent by Harrier strike.

The SAS raid at Goose Green on the night of 20 May had largely occupied the attention of the defenders who fancied themselves the target of a landing in at least battalion strength. On West Falkland, three army Pumas and an Agusta 109 attempting a redeployment of troops of the 8th Infantry Regiment from Fox Bay to

Port Howard on the morning of 23 May, were intercepted by Harriers and destroyed.

In anticipation of the coming attack on Darwin the Argentines had heli-lifted a company of the 25th Infantry Regiment from Stanley to Goose Green between 22 and 26 May, the 601st Special Forces Group simultaneously reconnoitering the British perimeter at San Carlos although avoiding contact.

The first major contact between the opposing ground forces came on the night of 27 May and the morning of 28 May when patrols clashed north of Darwin. The Argentine patrols fell back upon Darwin where the bulk of their forces were entrenched in positions carefully but unimaginatively prepared in strict accordance with military text books. Although outnumbering the attacking British paratroops by almost 2:1 they had been already softened up by bombardment from HMS *Arrow*, later reinforced by Harrier strikes. From first light their own Pucarás flew continuous ground attack missions against the advancing British, three falling victim to ground fire although two pilots ejected safely. The naval Macchis from Stanley also flew at least one ground support mission, one aircraft being shot down by a Blowpipe missile and its pilot killed.

On the ground the British paratroops advanced using the shock troop tactics perfected by the Germans in the latter stages of the First World War. The imaginative but unorthodox use of anti-tank rockets and Milan missiles for trench cleaning caused terror amongst the defenders and after an unsuccessful counterattack Darwin had surrendered by mid-morning. The British advance had however slowed down by mid afternoon and ground almost to a halt with the approach of darkness. Argentine demoralisation was now fairly complete however and before hostilities could resume the following day, Air Commodore Pedrozo requested a parley and later in the morning approximately 800 Army and 200 Air Force troops surrendered. Argentine losses had been approximately 50 dead and not 250 as indicated by contemporary reports, plus 150 wounded.

Burying the dead after the first engagements; even the Chaplain has been injured.

**The end of the affair; a Royal Marine disarming Argentine
soldiers as they pass into captivity.**

The outer defensive ring of Stanley began to come
under heavy air attack from 30 May and naval
bombardment once more became a regular occurence.

Although Stanley was now under almost continuous
naval bombardment little contact had still occurred
between the opposing land forces since Goose Green.
On 31 May opposing patrols made contact in the region
of Mount Kent and the outer defensive perimeter of
Stanley came under British artillery fire.

On 2 June the Argentines pulled back from Fitzroy.
On 10 June a brisk fire-fight took place between a
section of the 602nd Commando Company and British
Marines at Top Malo House north-west of Stanley, the
seven Argentine survivors only surrendering after their
nine comrades had been killed and their ammunition
exhausted. At about this time two Exocet launchers,
dismounted from the damaged frigate *Guerrico*, were
flown into Stanley and mounted on a trailer.

General Menéndez had deployed the 4th Infantry on Two Sisters ridge, Mount Harriet and Mount Kent, to the west of Stanley. The 7th Infantry, reinforced by the 602nd Commando Company, held Mount Longdon and Wireless Ridge to the north, while the 5th Marines were responsible for the defence of Tumbledown, Mount William and Sapper Hill to the south-west. The 25th Infantry held Stanley airport and the beaches to the south-east, which were considered the most likely site for a British landing. A company of the 6th Infantry Regiment occupied the ridge between Two Sisters and Mount Longdon, another company, together with a company of the 1st Infantry completing the defensive line to the south-east and the 3rd Infantry was deployed to the south of Sapper Hill.

The bulk of the 4th Artillery Group was stationed to the west of Stanley, with one battery sharing Stanley racecourse with a 105 mm battery of the 3rd Artillery, a battery of the latter unit being based at Moody Brook barracks. The anti-aircraft units were deployed in the vicinity of Stanley itself and at the airport. The armoured vehicles and heavy artillery were held in reserve in the town, the latter being principally employed for counter-battery fire against the British naval bombardment.

'B' Company of the 7th Infantry on Mount Longdon were quickly overrun, a counterattack by 'C' Company bogging down at 2.00 am. Meanwhile 'B' Company of the 4th Infantry was overrun on Mount Harriet. Throughout the day most of the remaining Argentine positions held, snipers from the 601st Commando Company proving particularly deadly opponents for the British in the Sapper Hill sector. On Two Sisters 'C' company of the 4th Infantry was overrun, the bulk of the Regiment holding. However by sundown Goat Ridge and Mount Wall had also been lost.

While these engagements were in progress an Exocet was launched from the improvised trailer, causing serious damage to HMS *Glamorgan* which was bombarding Stanley.

The defensive line was now contracting and Wireless Ridge, held by the remnants of the 7th Infantry Regiment and a company of the 3rd Infantry, reinforced by the 10th Armoured Cavalry Reconnaissance Squadron fighting as infantry, came under attack and despite a partially successful counter attack had been forced to yield ground by dawn on 14 June. The 5th Marines, holding the slopes of Mount Tumbledown, were now surrounded on three sides, providing the most tenacious resistance of any Argentine ground forces throughout the campaign although after an unsuccessful counterattack they were forced to withdraw to Sapper Hill. Most of the Argentine artillery was by now out of action, the British light guns having a 50 per cent greater range than their OTO Melaras and being able to pick them off with impunity. The remnants of the Marines on Sapper Hill were virtually surrounded by 10.00 am and were forced to retreat.

With the British occupying all of the high ground around Stanley the inner defensive line now broke, demoralised troops leaving their positions and streaming into the town. Further resistance was hopeless and at 8.59 pm General Menéndez formally surrendered the surviving 10,254 Argentine troops in the islands. During the campaign the Argentines had suffered 1241 killed and 1046 wounded.

Grenades

Owen Carrow

Grenades have a long history but one which is distinguished by several ups and downs; as a weapon of war they seem to move in and out of fashion with different armies at different times. The grenade first appeared in the 16th century, a spherical container of earthenware or glass filled with gunpowder and with a quickmatch fuze. The 'grenadier' lit the fuze and threw the grenade; if the length of the fuze was correct and the thrower skilled, then the grenade would burst as it arrived among the enemy. If the thrower got it wrong, then there was a possibility that the grenade would shatter when it landed and fail to have much effect or, worse, an astute and bold enemy might pick it up and throw it back; it might not reach the thrower but at least it would go off harmlessly, in the wrong place.

By the middle of the 19th century the grenade was in one of its declines; it had lost its place in open warfare and was retained principally as a defensive measure for fortresses. The British *Treatise on Ammunition* of the 1880s said, somewhat dismissively, 'They are used chiefly for the defence of places against assault, being thrown among the storming parties in the ditch.' It went on to say, 'When men are using them they should be cautioned not to retain the grenade too long in their hands', a piece of advice which still has some considerable force.

The Russo-Japanese War brought the grenade back into active service. The Japanese troops besieging Port Arthur found time hanging heavy on their hands in their trenches ringing the fortress, and began amusing themselves by filling bottles with explosive, adding a primitive fuze of much the same origin as the 16th century quickmatch, and throwing them at the Russians in the adjacent trenches. The Russians retaliated in kind, and eventually the respective ordnance services began manufacturing official and rather safer devices.

The Russo-Japanese War was probably the last major conflict to which neutrals sent 'observers' to attach

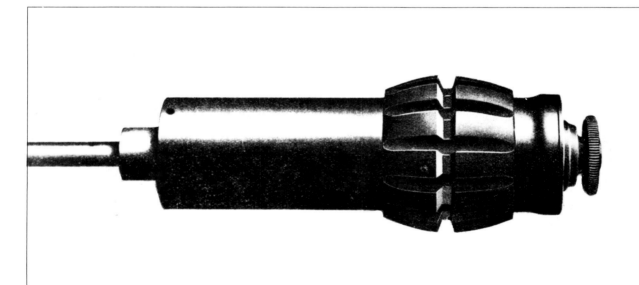

Hale's original rifle grenade. The rod was about half a metre long, and the hand-thrown version had a bunch of streamers in its place.

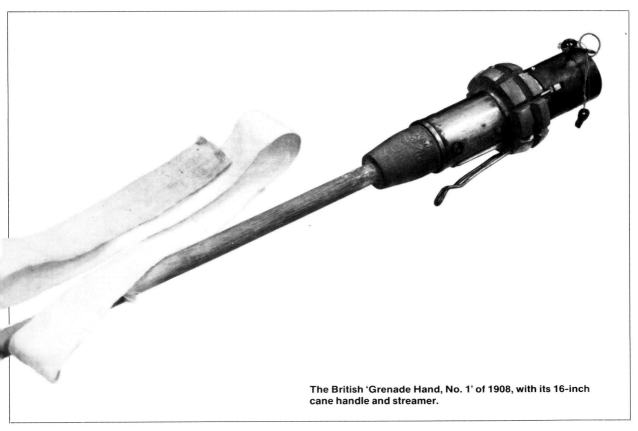

The British 'Grenade Hand, No. 1' of 1908, with its 16-inch cane handle and streamer.

themselves to the belligerent armies to watch how they went about making war. Officers from almost every major army were attached to each side (some armies managed to place observers with both sides) and they duly reported back to their respective War Departments as to what their hosts were doing, what tactics were being employed, what weapons were in use, and what effect the weapons and tactics were having. As a result of these observers most armies were informed of the tactical use of machine guns, barbed wire and other innovations, and, of course, about the use of grenades.

The information was also spread by war correspondents, and the first designer to take up the idea appears to have been a British explosives engineer called Martin Hale. In 1908 he staged a demonstration of his designs for the various Military Attachés of the foreign embassies in London. Hand and rifle grenades were shown off, and these were basically of the same design, differing only in the manner of protecting them. They were simple brass tubes carrying a four-ounce charge of 'Tonite', a patented blasting explosive which was principally composed of guncotton. Inside the explosive was a central tube containing a weighted firing pin, restrained by a spring from making contact with a mining detonator. Around the tube was a cast-iron ring, deeply scored so as to break up into lethal fragments when the tube full of explosive detonated.

Due to the construction of the firing system it was necessary that the grenade landed on one specific end, so that the inertia of the needle would overcome the spring and impale the detonator. In order to achieve this the hand grenade had a rope tail attached, by which it was flung and which streamed out behind during flight to ensure arrival in the correct attitude. This could be thrown some thirty metres. To obtain more range there was a rifle-launched version which used the same basic grenade attached to a thin steel rod which was inserted into the muzzle of a rifle. The rifleman then loaded a blank cartridge into the chamber of the weapon, braced the butt of the rifle against the ground and pulled the trigger; the explosion of the blank cartridge generated sufficient gas to blow the rod and the grenade from the barrel and send the grenade about 250 metres distance. The rod acted as the stabiliser, again ensuring that the grenade landed nose-first.

The Spanish Army bought some numbers of these grenades and used them in Morocco, while the German Army bought a lesser number 'for evaluation'. The British Army politely declined to buy, since they were already at work on their own design. In those days the design departments of most armies were reluctant to purchase any warlike store from 'trade' if they could develop something as good in their own workshops; largely, one supposes, in order to avoid paying patent

153

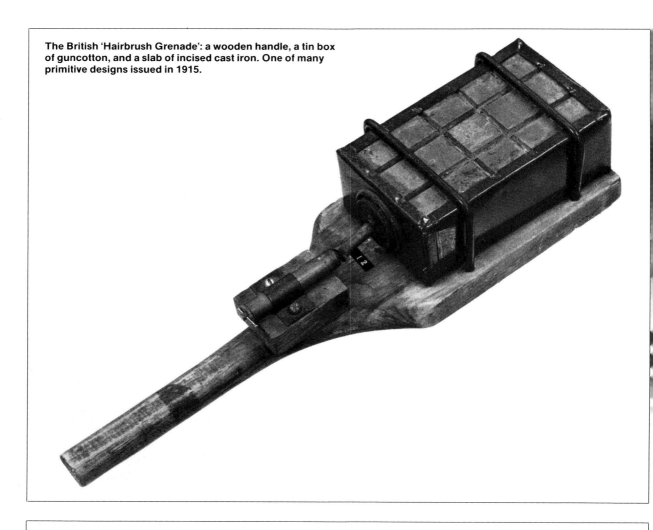

The British 'Hairbrush Grenade': a wooden handle, a tin box of guncotton, and a slab of incised cast iron. One of many primitive designs issued in 1915.

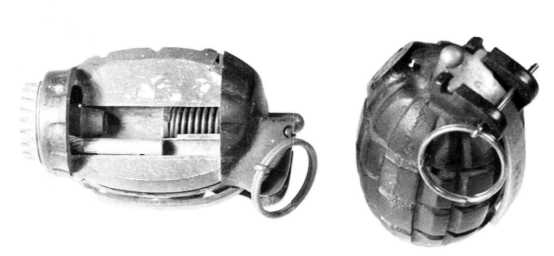

The 'Mills Bomb', complete and sectioned to show the striker and detonator.

The German stick grenade. The screwed cap at the end of the stick was removed to expose the cord which fired the igniter.

A German soldier loading a rifle grenade into a cup discharger.

and licence fees. The patented feature of Hale's design was the arrangement of striker and detonator, and the British got round this by reversing the action in a somewhat primitive manner. The grenade had a similar brass tube with cast-iron ring, but the head carried a recess leading into the centre of the explosive charge. Into this recess went a mining detonator, and then a cap was slipped on top of the tube. This had a steel needle in its centre, posed above the detonator, and the two were kept apart by the cap having grooves which corresponded to lugs on the tube; set in the 'safe' position the lugs and grooves formed a block which prevented needle and detonator from contacting, but when turned to 'fire' the grooves lined up with the lugs so as to allow the cap to be driven down, causing the detonator to be fired. Again, the design demanded that the grenade land on its nose, and to ensure this the tube was fitted with a 16-inch cane handle and four cloth streamers.

This device was officially introduced as 'Grenade, Hand, Mark I' in June 1908, and it was doubtless thrown at annual training camps in the subsequent years with no complaints. But when the British Army found

155

itself in the trenches in 1914, the design soon exhibited a fundamental drawback. The soldier would seize his grenade by its 16-inch handle, remove the safety pin, twist the cap to 'fire', swing his arm back to throw – and promptly smash the head of the grenade against the rear wall of the trench, blowing himself and his companions to pieces. It didn't take many accidents of that nature to get the 'Grenade, Hand, Mark I' a bad name among the British Expeditionary Force.

I have spent some time describing these early grenades since they illustrate some of the design fundamentals which must still be borne in mind by designers. The device has to be safe while in the hands of the thrower, arm itself in flight, and go off unfailingly when it arrives at the target; it should be so designed, too, that should the thrower be shot in mid-throw and drop the grenade, it should remain safe. It should not be possible for the recipient to pick it up and throw it back. It is preferable that it should not require any stabilising devices but should work effectively irrespective of the angle at which it lands. It is further desirable that it should be capable of being sent to longer distances by means of a rifle. You might think this a fairly reasonable and simple catalogue of requests, but in fact reconciling them into a practical package has taxed designers' brains for years.

It soon became apparent that impact fuzing – designing the grenade to detonate when it struck the target – was difficult, since it almost always ended up with a need for stabilisation. Time fuzing, on the other hand, meant that anything which could be thrown would work, provided the timing was accurate and not too long. The famous 'Mills Bomb' of 1915 appears to have been the first really acceptable solution. This used a rimfire cap attached to a short length of safety fuze, leading to a detonator. This was fitted into the grenade so that the cap sat at the bottom of a central tube; above it was a striker held, against a powerful spring, by a steel lever which in turn was locked by a safety pin. The thrower took the grenade in his hand so that he held the lever against the grenade body, and removed the pin; then he threw it. The striker spring drove the striker down, throwing the lever off as it did so, and fired the cap. This lit the fuze, which burned for four seconds and then fired the detonator, which in turn set off the explosive in the grenade. Various lengths of fuze were tried, but four seconds became the norm, since it was long enough to allow the grenade to be thrown to its maximum distance (about 35 metres) but not so long that it could be picked up and thrown back.

The Mills also introduced the familiar serrated iron casing, used on innumerable designs since then. It is popularly believed to control the fragmentation of the

Firing a modern rifle grenade from the muzzle of the FN-FAL semi-automatic rifle.

grenade, but examination of the fragments shows that it never does; in fact, a close reading of Mills' original patents shows that his idea was to provide a safe grip for muddy hands in the trenches of Flanders.

The Germans introduced the 'stick' grenade, a metal canister on the end of a wooden handle. Inside the bottom of the canister was a friction igniter, a length of fuze and a detonator. Running through the hollow handle was a cord attached to the igniter. On pulling this a jagged pin was pulled through a match composition, lighting the detonator, whereupon the grenade was thrown, to burst after about four seconds. It is another popular belief that having a handle allows the grenade to be thrown further, but again, practical trials have shown that in the hands of trained soldiers there is very little difference between the distance a stick grenade or a Mills grenade can be thrown.

Discharging grenades by means of rods thrust down rifles had by then been found to have detrimental effects on the rifles, and the cup discharger was born. This was a large-calibre cup attached to the muzzle of the rifle, into which a grenade could be placed and the safety pin removed. A blank cartridge fired in the rifle generated gas to blow the grenade from the cup, leaving the rifle in a fit condition to fire ordinary bullets from if need be. The French developed a unique grenade for rifle firing, one with a hole down its centre-line. This removed the need to use a blank cartridge; an ordinary ball bullet was fired, and as it passed through the centre hole so it tripped a striker and ignited the grenade fuze, while the gas following the bullet launched the grenade.

The Second World War was fought largely with the same grenades which had proved their worth in the First, though they had seen some slight improvements in the intervening years. But the war brought some new tactics and new problems, and hence some new grenades were devised to deal with them. First came the anti-tank grenade, either rifle-fired or hand-thrown. If the former, it relied on the shaped charge principle; if the latter, it generally relied on nothing more than placing a sizeable amount of explosive on the tank and hoping for the best. The first to show some ingenuity were the German Army with a shaped charge grenade fitted with magnets, so that when thrown at a tank it adhered to the armour in the correct attitude to penetrate. The British developed a grenade which consisted of a glass sphere filled with nitro-glycerine and coated with a sticky adhesive. It was protected by two tin hemispheres which were released immediately before throwing, but in practice, unless the thrower was extremely careful, it frequently stuck to his clothing during his preliminary swing, and as a result there is no known record of it ever being used in combat.

By 1945 there was a considerable body of information available on the subject of grenades, and some rethinking due. For some years it had been customary to divide anti-personnel grenades into two classes, offensive

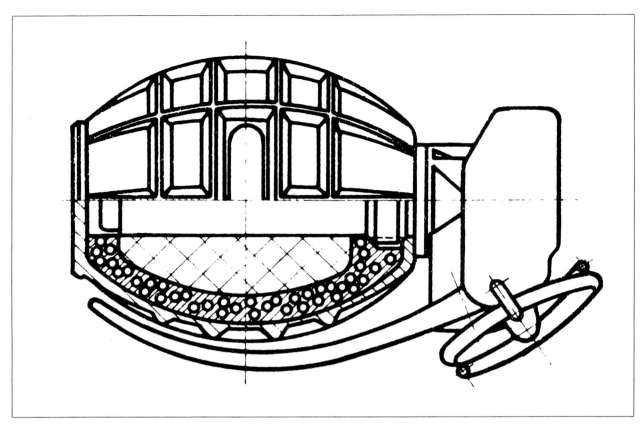

Drawing of a modern hand grenade, showing the layer of pre-formed fragments, set in plastic, around the main explosive charge. The outer casing is of plastic, formed to give a good grip for the thrower.

and defensive. The difference between the two lay in the fragment-producing capabilities. The offensive grenade was one which delivered small fragments to a short distance, so that a soldier moving forward – on the offensive – could throw it without the need to protect himself against its effects, since the fragments would not come back far enough to endanger him. The defensive grenade, on the other hand, was to be used by a man in a defensive position who could throw the grenade and take cover against its effects, since its fragments would be large and would fly further than the throwing distance. Unfortunately it was not unknown for an offensive grenade to throw a rogue fragment over a considerable distance, or for a defensive grenade to have small effect; the results were almost random since the only design difference was the thickness of the grenade's casing. A thin case meant small light fragments and short range – most of the time, while a thick case meant big fragments and a longer range – again, most of the time.

The war had led to some advances in the technology of explosives, and one area which had been well explored was that of controlling the fragmentation of various types of projectile. Some of this spun off to the

grenade design offices, and just as the war ended the US Army began testing an entirely new type of grenade. Instead of simply making a metal casing and allowing the explosive to do what it liked, the explosive was surrounded by a casing made of coiled and notched steel rod, the tensile strength of which was carefully matched

to the power of the explosive. This was then covered with a thin steel casing, and the usual type of fly-off lever fuze fitted into the centre of the explosive. When thrown, the explosive detonated and the notched rod parted at the notches to provide several thousand precisely-sized fragments, each of a carefully calculated weight such that, given the velocity derived from the explosive, its flight distance would be predictable. Moreover, since the detonator was central and the yield strength of the notched steel rod evenly distributed, the fragments would spread in a regular pattern all around the grenade. Nothing within five metres would live, nothing within ten metres would escape unscathed,

The dual-purpose grenade. On the left, the basic offensive grenade with plastic casing and containing pre-formed fragments; centre, the fragmentation sleeve, and right, the two put together to provide a defensive grenade.

The 'Polyvalent' grenade: left, configured for rifle firing, right with the tail unit removed as a hand grenade.

A rocket-assisted rifle grenade. The fins open after launch to give additional stability, and the rocket motor, which gives additional range, is contained in the tail tube.

The American 40 mm M406 high explosive grenade. The streamlined head contains the fuze; the internally-grooved grenade body is beneath it; and the round is completed by the cartridge case.

while anything fifteen metres away would be entirely untouched. This device went into service as the M26 grenade and has remained the primary US grenade ever since, as well as beng copied by several other countries, Britain among them.

The M26 and its siblings were satisfactory as general purpose grenades, but there were still those who preferred the old distinction of offensive and defensive, and in the postwar years several manufacturers found a solution to this. The preferred answer was to produce an offensive grenade of plastic, filled with pre-formed fragments; these were small steel balls or cubes set into a matrix of plastic around the explosive filling, the whole being encased in a plastic outer cover. Used as an offensive grenade this gave the same closely-controlled radius of action, due to careful selection of the fragment size and careful matching to the type of explosive used. When it was necessary to use a defensive grenade, a fragmentation sleeve of steel or cast iron could be slipped over the body of the basic grenade, and the subsequent detonation would rend this into heavy fragments, though with a less predictable danger area.

The anti-personnel rifle grenade had declined in favour during the 1939-45 war, but the need for an anti-tank weapon for the infantryman had led to the rifle-launching technique being kept alive, though in general the rifle anti-tank grenade was insufficient to cause much damage to tanks by 1945. For anti-personnel use one common resort was to produce a tail unit to which a standard hand grenade could be clipped; this could then be loaded over an extension attached to a rifle muzzle, and the combination launched by means of a blank cartridge.

In the postwar years most armies rejected the rifle grenade as being incapable of doing anything of value; most armies had small mortars, of the 50-60 mm calibre range, carried by infantry platoons and capable of being brought into action rapidly when a short-range bomb was required, and thus the rifle grenade languished. Another reason for this abandonment was simply that the rifle grenade was usually somewhat heavy, and while firing it from an old-style bolt-action rifle was more or less acceptable, firing them from the new semi-automatic rifles entering service in the 1950s set up far too much stress and rapidly shook the rifles to pieces.

The private manufacturers, rather than the armies, found the solution to this dilemma; again, a matter of controlled fragmentation. Instead of making the grenade with a heavy cast-iron head, it was made with a thin alloy or steel head, covering a lining of pre-formed fragments around an explosive charge. This warhead was then attached to a tail tube with fins which would slide over the muzzle of a rifle and could be fired off in the usual way. Due to the reduced weight of the warhead the recoil force was reduced and less stress placed on the rifle.

It was at this point that one of the most remarkable examples of standardisation came about, and it happened entirely as a private arrangement between grenade makers and rifle makers. The internal diameter of the grenade tail tube and the external diameter of rifle barrels were standardized, so that today it is possible to fire almost any rifle grenade from almost any rifle, irrespective of where the two items were manufactured. Eventually it became a NATO standard, even though all NATO armies do not fire rifle grenades.

One final improvement to the rifle grenade has been

the addition of a bullet trap in the tail. Ever since rifle grenades were first used, there has always been an element of hazard in the possibility of a soldier loading a ball cartridge into his rifle to fire the grenade, instead of the regulation blank. Moreover the business of emptying the rifle's chamber and reloading it with a blank, then reloading again with ball, is something the soldier, in the heat of battle, could do without. Incorporating a bullet trap into the grenade tail tube means that there is now no requirement to load a blank cartridge; the standard ball bullet, which is probably already loaded into the rifle's chamber, can be used. The bullet is caught and held by the trap, an arrangement of frangible plates which gradually collapse around the bullet and hold it; its energy is given up to the grenade, and at the same time the gases propelling

the bullet expand into the tail tube and give the grenade its launching impulse. Since the charge used with a ball bullet is not the optimum for grenade launching, the grenade will usually have a slightly lesser maximum range, but this is considered a small trade-off for the convience of not having to carry a supply of blank cartridges around – and probably finding none when the need arose.

Loading a 40 mm grenade into the M203 launcher, mounted under the barrel of an M16 rifle.

The shaped charge anti-tank grenade has also benefited from improvements in technology. Whereas the British Grenade No 68 of 1940 could penetrate 50 mm of armour, modern rifle grenades can pierce anything from 100 mm to 275 mm depending upon the diameter of their warhead. No rifle grenade, though, is expected to have much effect against the frontal armour of a modern main battle tank; the best the infantryman can hope for is to be able to attack the tank from the rear, where the armour is thinner, and perhaps damage the engine. A more likely and profitable use of the rifle grenade will be against armoured personnel carriers and similar types of light armoured vehicle which abound on today's battlefield.

Fuzing has also seen improvements due to modern technology. Throughout most of its career the grenade has been timed by nothing more sophisticated than a length of black powder fuze, though it must be admitted that constant refining had brought it to a highly reliable standard. Rifle grenades were invariably fuzed to detonate on impact, though the combination hand-and-rifle designs retained the time fuze system, albeit using a longer time to allow for the longer trajectory. In recent years, though, electric fuzes have begun to appear on hand grenades and it is probable that before the end of the decade the pyrotechnic fuze will be obsolete.

The Soviet AGS-17 automatic grenade launcher.

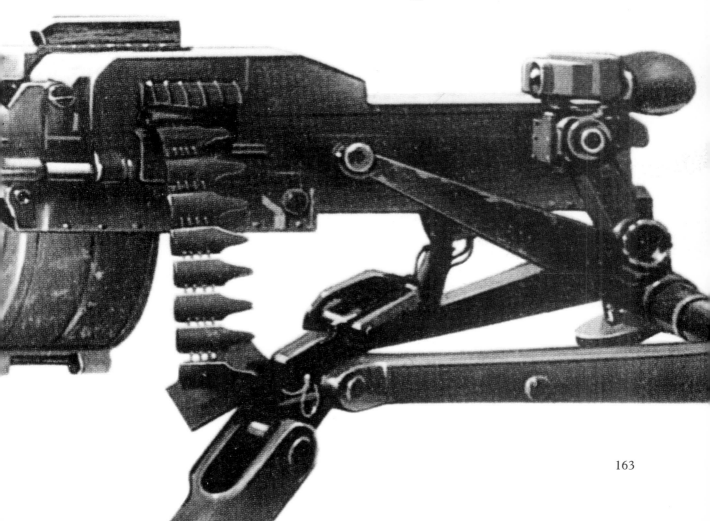

The American Mark 19 'machine gun', showing the grenades being fed in by belt.

The electric fuze can be made to work in a number of ways. The American M217 fuze, used with their M68 hand grenade, has the usual fly-off lever to ignite both a powder train and a thermal power supply. After a brief delay, during which time the thermal power supply is building up sufficient voltage, the electrical system is fully armed and thereafter impact of the grenade at the target will cause a simple inertia switch to close and detonate the explosive charge. Should the impact fail to operate the switch, the powder train continues to burn and after seven seconds detonates the grenade. A British design, by Ferranti, uses a fly-off lever to release a soft iron core through a magnetic circuit; this generates a pulse of electrical energy which is then stored in a capacitor. Impact at the target is sensed by an inertia switch which closes and allows the capacitor to discharge into a detonator. Another version uses the capacitor to charge a timing circuit which, after four seconds, fires the detonator. Another British design, this time by Haley & Weller, uses a small battery inside the fuze unit to provide power; when the grenade is thrown

the fly-off lever moves sufficiently far to close a switch, allowing power to flow from the battery to an electronic timing circuit, which fires the detonator after a short delay.

It will have been noted that all these electrical fuzes retain the fly-off lever, even though the operation of the fuze could easily be controlled by other methods. This is simply so that soldiers who have been accustomed to the lever system need not be retrained on some new method of arming a grenade. So far as the soldier is concerned, he treats all hand grenades in the same fashion; remove the pin, hold the lever down, and throw. How the grenade works is of little interest to him, so long as it works reliably.

The anti-personnel rifle grenade is tactically satisfactory when fired by an impact fuze for perhaps 60 percent of the time; the remaining 40 percent of targets would be better attacked if the grenade could be made to burst in the air above the target, so showering the area with fragments. Hitherto this would have meant expensive and complex timing devices, and impossibly precise control of the trajectory, and therefore it has been considered impractical. But, once again, modern technology has provided an answer, and two European companies are currently developing simple opto-electronic proximity fuzes for use in rifle grenades. In broad outline, these rely upon optical sensors to detect the closeness of the ground or any solid target, after which the electronic circuitry takes over and detonates the grenade at a height best calculated to distribute its fragments over a useful lethal area. At present these devices are at an advanced state of development, and there are doubtless several technical questions, and certainly the question of cost-effectiveness, to be settled.

But the rifle grenade is currently struggling to hold its place against an entirely different type of grenade, the American-designed 40 mm type which is now being taken into service in several armies throughout the world. This was developed in the 1960s and is simply a small pre-fragmented grenade concealed, together with an impact fuze, in a streamlined projectile which is fired from a small shoulder gun. The grenade is attached to a cartridge case and loaded into the weapon rather in the manner of a shotgun; due to the design of the propelling charge system the recoil is tolerable, and the grenade can be fired to ranges up to 300 metres with good accuracy. As well as being fired from a dedicated weapon, the M72 grenade launcher, it can also be fired from a truncated gun which is attached beneath the barrel of a rifle, so that any man with a rifle can be a grenadier, and the man launching the grenades also has a rifle for personal defence.

The latest move in this type of grenade is the development of special machine guns to fire them. This was explored briefly by the US Army in the late 1960s, but with the ending of the Vietnam war the interest in this type of device waned. It was then taken up by the Russians, who developed a 37 mm grenade similar in form to the American type and an automatic grenade launcher to go with it. Once this was revealed, American interest was rekindled, and in the late 1970s the Mark 19 40 mm machine gun appeared. These allow a stream of grenades to be fired, giving close support to the infantry squad. But when one gets to this type of weapon it becomes very difficult for the layman to distinguish between a grenade launcher and a good old-fashioned gun, and perhaps the barrier has been crossed and we are talking about artillery.

100 Years Ago

In the 1870s the US Congress ceased to allocate money for coast defence; the reason for this was partly financial stringency in the wake of the Civil War and partly because the development of weapons and fortification was in something of a flux during that period. American engineers could point to Europe where forts and defences were being dismantled before they were finished in order to accommodate new and more powerful guns or to conform with the latest tactical ideas, and argue, with some justification, that spending

10-inch disappearing guns at Fort Casey, Puget Sound, one of the many forts which were built as a result of the Endicott Board's deliberations. (*Washington State Parks & Recreation Commission*)

money on defences would be wasteful until the armament and form of such defences could be positively defined.

By the early 1880s, however, foreign progress in naval construction gave rise to alarm, and in 1885 President Cleveland assembled a special Board under the chairmanship of Secretary of War William C. Endicott to review the coast defence situation and submit recommendations for a programme based on the latest fortification theories and the latest designs of weapons. The Board was composed of Army and Navy officers and civil engineering experts and devoted several months to a thorough study of the entire subject.

On 23 January 1886 the Endicott Board (as it was thereafter known) submitted its report. This called for a massive programme of construction and armament covering the East and West coasts, the Gulf of Mexico

and even the Great Lakes, a total of 29 defended localities, plus floating batteries, torpedo boats and submarine mines. The total cost of this was put at $126 million, a staggering sum for those days, but, as with similar Boards and Commissions which sat in other countries in the latter half of the 19th century, the recommendations were overtaken by events. The Board made extremely detailed plans for the individual forts, down to the numbers of guns and types of mounting, thickness of walls and capacity of magazines, but even as they reported the ordnance engineers were developing more powerful weapons and advanced types of mounting, so that the original recommendations were scrapped almost as fast as they appeared. Nevertheless, the broad application of the plan was closely adhered to, the details being altered as mechanical improvements made their appearance.

One major change was that the increasing power of the guns being developed allowed a considerable reduction in armament strength. Where it was first considered necessary to plant a large number of guns around a harbour in order to be able to fire into every stretch of water, guns of increased range allowed the number of emplacements to be reduced, though the area was still being effectively covered. As a result the original recommendation, for some 1300 guns and mortars of over 8-inch calibre, was eventually reduced to just under 700 pieces of ordnance.

Perhaps the most significant feature of the Endicott Board proposals was the fundamental change in the nature of fortification. Hitherto a fort had been a latterday descendant of a mediaeval castle, a stone building raised above the surrounding area, perhaps with armoured gun ports, and with the armament securely inside casemates. The drawback with this form of construction, as had been discovered in Europe, was that once the fort had been designed and built around a particular type of armament, any improvements in gun construction, leading to longer or bigger guns, meant that the new armament frequently would not fit into the spaces in the fort. Moreover these stark rectangular edifices were easily seen from the sea and made excellent targets, even for the primitive naval gunnery of the day.

But the forts devised by the Endicott Board were of a totally different form: instead of being buildings containing concentrations of guns, they now became areas of real estate containing gun emplacements sunk into the ground and widely dispersed so as to blend in with the landscape. Linked with the development of disappearing gun carriages, which lowered the gun into its emplacement and out of sight when not being fired, this meant that the observer at sea found nothing of prominence to use as an aiming mark. Guns simply appeared for a few seconds, fired, and vanished into the ground, leaving nothing but a drifting cloud of smoke to mark their location, and at long range even this was a

168

The first 9-inch rifled muzzle loading high-angle gun, before being sent to the Isle of Wight for trial.

poor indication. Instead of sailing into a harbour and instantly identifying all the defences, it was now impossible to gauge what the defences were until they actually opened fire.

Another result of this form of construction was a reversal of the relative costs of works and armament; prior to the 1880s the major expense in constructing a fort lay in the masonry and armour plate, in the ratio of about seven to one against the cost of the guns. With the improved ordnance and complex mountings of the post-1880 era, together with the simplified nature of the actual works, a ratio changed to about one to two – the armament cost twice as much as the real estate and concrete.

But in 1886 all this was in the future. Although the Endicott Board specified types of gun and mounting, it was to be several years before designs were perfected, and construction to the Board's recommendations did not begin until the early 1890s.

In Britain work had been going forward on coast defences for twenty years, and the country was well provided with granite forts with casemated guns at all the major naval bases. But in 1884 the Inspector-General of Fortifications had suggested that it might be advantageous to change the method of attacking warships. Instead of firing heavy guns against their side armour, which was getting thicker every year, might it not be a good idea to fire shells up into the air so that they fell steeply on to the thinner deck armour, so achieving penetration into the vitals of the ship? He suggested using old rifled muzzle-loading 9-inch guns, mounting them so that they could fire at 70° angle of elevation. The idea was examined, considered worth pursuing, and during 1885-86 a 9-inch gun was suitably modified and tested. Initial firing tests for range and accuracy showed that it was possible to reach out to 10,000 yards with a good chance of hitting something as big as a warship's deck, and in May 1886 a trial was fired against an armour-plate target 20ft by 13ft and three inches thick, laid flat on the ground at the Shoeburyness Experimental Establishment. It was 3000 yards from the gun and was hit and penetrated on the seventh shot of the trial. This result was so heartening that it was decided to bore out another gun to 10-inch calibre and rifle it, so as to fire a heavier shell. The Ordnance Committee, in their report, observed that 'Sufficient accuracy will be obtained to compel the enemy's ships to keep on the move, and thus impair the accuracy of their fire'.

The use of high-angle guns (often called 'mortars' in other countries) for coast defence soon became an accepted practice, though it was not until the middle 1890s that batteries were built, due to several years spent in trials and in developing a suitable fire control system. The idea was widely embraced in other countries too, the United States eventually mounting over 700 12-inch

mortars in coast defences, and German, French and Japanese forts also employing them. Strangely, the idea was never embraced with very much enthusiasm in Britain. The rifled muzzle loading 10-inch guns stayed in service until the 1920s, though most were replaced by a more modern design of 9.2-inch breech-loading high-angle gun shortly before the First World War, but even these were declared obsolete in 1929 and the high angle coast defence gun was seen no more in British service. The principal objection seems to have been the difficulty of fire control and the consequent lack of accuracy. Most countries got over this by mounting them in groups of four and firing salvos from four groups at once, so as to drench the target with 16 shells,

The original drawings, dated 23 September 1886, of Very's Signal Pistol and its associated cartridge.

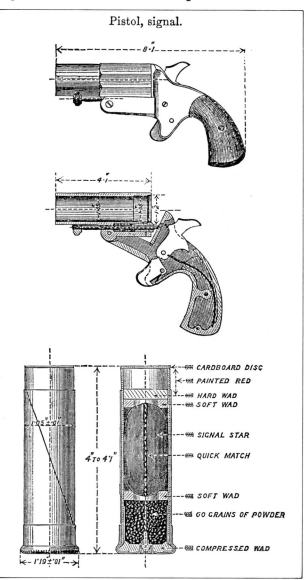

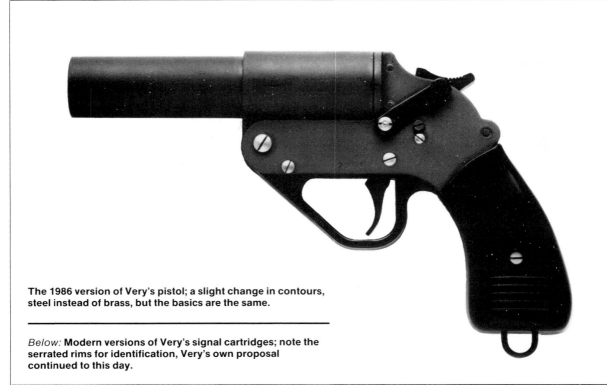

The 1986 version of Very's pistol; a slight change in contours, steel instead of brass, but the basics are the same.

Below: Modern versions of Very's signal cartridges; note the serrated rims for identification, Very's own proposal continued to this day.

but the British practice, doubtless due to shortage of funds, was to use four-gun muzzle-loading or two-gun breech-loading batteries, so placing a premium on a degree of accuracy which wasn't obtainable.

It is not often that we can find a piece of equipment introduced 100 years ago which, in essentials, is still in everyday service, but List of Changes Para. 5181, approved 23 September 1886, is a rare example:-

'Pistol, Signal, Brass, Very's cartridge. A pattern of this pistol has been sealed for Naval service. It is intended for firing the signal cartridge described in Para 5173. The barrel drops at right-angles for loading and extracting. The body and barrel are made of brass and are left bright'.

The cartridges were available with red, green or white stars, and for recognition in the dark had milled or part-milled rims – a method of identification still employed. Very was a Lieutenant in the United States Navy and developed the pistol and its cartridge in the late 1870s. His selection of one inch as the calibre must have been inspired, since it has remained the standard ever since, and the modern signal pistol and associated cartridge show little difference from the original design.

Although Hiram Maxim was by now hard at work promoting his automatic machine gun, mechanical designs still held the stage since they were, if not high technology, at least known to work. The Gatling and Gardner designs having been in service for some time, they were joined in June 1885 by the Nordenfelt gun. This original introduction was for the Royal Navy, but their use was extended to the army soon afterwards.

The Nordenfelt was actually designed by a man called Helge Palmkranz, a Swedish engineer, but in order to finance his invention he went to a banker, Torsten Nordenfelt, and part of the price of financial support was that the weapon was henceforth known by the backer's name instead of that of the inventor. It originally appeared in one-inch calibre in 1880 but the gun which entered British service in 1885 was the first rifle-calibre model, firing the standard 0.45-inch Martini-Henry cartridge.

The Nordenfelt was a multiple-barrel weapon: two to 10 barrels lay alongside each other, their breech ends inside a receiver unit. Operation was by a lever alongside the receiver which was pushed back and forth by the gunner. On the forward stroke a carrier block, which carried cartridges delivered from an overhead hopper, was moved into line with the barrels. A breech block then moved forward to chamber the rounds, and an action block, containing the firing pins, moved in behind the breech block and lined up with the caps of the cartridges. As the handle reached the end of its forward stroke the firing pins were tripped and the barrels fired. On the return stroke of the lever the action block moved away, the breech opened and ejected the

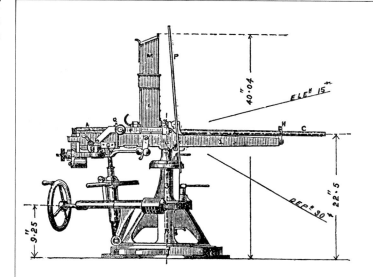

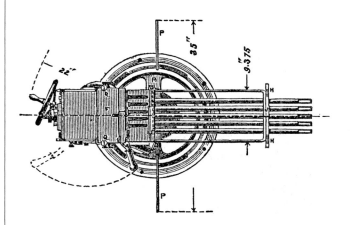

Original drawings of the Nordenfelt machine gun, on a cone mounting for use in warships.

empty cartridge cases, and the carrier block moved across to recharge itself from the hopper. The action was simple and robust, and the Nordenfelt gun, in various calibres, remained in service until 1903. The rate of fire depended, of course, on how many barrels the gun had and how rapidly the lever was worked, but as an example Nordenfelt himself, demonstrating a 10-barrel gun at Portsmouth in 1882, fired 3000 rounds in three minutes.

They appear, though, to have had their drawbacks: a report by Capt W. C. Savile, RA, on a trial of machine guns at Dartford on 9 July 1886:

'One great danger showed itself on more than one occasion. After "cease firing" was given the No 1 of the gun was forgetful to ascertain if there still remained any unexploded cartridges in his gun. A zealous person, wishing to make himself familiar

171

with the working of the gun found himself innocently blazing away into the crowd, nearly costing the army its Commander-in-Chief and your department its Assistant Superintendent of Experiments . . .'

In 1883 Wolseley managed to persuade the War Office that officers should perform field training with the troops they commanded. This led to some hurried scratching about for tactical instruction, leading eventually to List of Changes Para. 4949, approved 15 December 1885:

'Kriegspiel men, box of. A pattern box as above, with contents, has been sealed to govern supplies. It is fitted with two trays, each tray containing a set of 308 "men" for use in the war game. The men are small oblong pieces of type metal, varying in

enfelt machine gun on field mounting.

been taken from the German General Staff (hence the name), and it remained in vogue for several years.

The cat-o-nine tails and the triangle had been done away with, but that didn't mean life was getting any softer for the errant soldier: List of Changes Para. 4996, approved 19 May 1885:

> 'Bed, Plank, for military prisons. A pattern of the above-mentioned article has been sealed to govern supplies for provost and garrison cells ... it is composed of three deal boards ⅞-inch thick, secured to three bearers, and having a fixed wooden pillow.'

These were still to be seen as part of the furniture of regimental guard rooms well into the 1960s, and for all I know some may be there yet.

In another part of the far-flung Empire, the prisoners were even worse off. Minute 42,768 of the Proceedings of the Department of the Director of Artillery:

> 'Commissary-General of Ordnance, 14.7.85, states that he has been called upon to supply "Irons, Leg, 22lb, Military Prison" for Egypt, and that there is no sealed pattern.
>
> Inspector-General of Military Prisons 16.9.85 says that these are illegal; "Chains, Restraint, Leg, 5½lb" should be used.'

And finally: in 1885-86 the Ordnance Committee were looking for a convenient portable range-finder for use by infantry and artillery, and had several designs submitted. Among them was one from a Major Whish; Minute 11,362 of 20 December 1886 refers:

> 'Major Whish, 16th Bengal Infantry, requests that he may be allowed to bring his rangefinder to England so that he may be certain that it is submitted to the Committee in proper order and also that he may give verbal explanation. He requests that a passage may be ordered and that his Indian pay may be continued.
>
> Director of Artillery asks whether the Committee consider the presence of Major Whish necessary?
>
> Committee inform Director of Artillery they see no necessity for the attendance of Major Whish.'

You have to give him credit for a damn good try.

size according to what they are intended to represent. One set is coloured red, the other blue'.

The descriptive paragraph then went on to detail all the various formations represented, from battalions in line (36) to sentries (15), batteries of 16-pr guns (3) and 'one-third of the Pontoon Train' (3). The pieces were used in conjunction with special maps issued by the Intelligence Department. The idea of *Kriegspiel* had